Bed I Beware

An easy to understand guide to bed bugs, their prevention and control

> "The walls were as thin as matchwood, and to hide the cracks they had been covered with layer after layer of pink paper, which had come loose and housed innumerable bugs. Near the ceiling long lines of bugs marched all day like columns of soldiers, and at night came down ravenously hungry, so that one had to get up every few hours and kill them in hecatombs. Sometimes when the bugs got too bad one used to burn sulphur and drive them into the next room; whereupon the lodger next door would retort by having his room sulphured, and drive the bugs back."
>
> George Orwell – Down and Out in Paris and London

Authors

David Cain PgCert, BSc (Hons) Esq
Richard Strand BSc (Hons), CBiol, MIBiol

# Contents

Frequently asked questions

If I get bitten at night does it mean I have bed bugs?
No, there are many different things that could have caused the bite, bed bugs being just one of them.

Do bed bugs carry disease?
No, although bed bugs can bite and draw blood they do not spread any diseases.

Do bed bugs fly?
No, bed bugs crawl around slowly but can walk on all but the smoothest of surfaces.

Do bed bugs jump?
No, bed bugs do not jump. If insects bite and jump they are usually fleas.

How far can a bed bug crawl?
Actually, quite a long distance in your house or hotel. They can move right around a single room and from room to room.

How big are bed bugs?
Adults are about 5mm long. The younger stages which are called nymphs are much smaller and look like small adults.

Can you see bed bugs?
Adult bed bugs are brown to reddish-brown, oval-shaped and flattened so you can see them. The younger stages; the nymphs, are often translucent so they are more difficult to detect.

Can they attach to my body or clothes?
Yes, they can get caught in the fibres of clothes, luggage and furniture. They feed on human blood but only attach to the body when they are actually feeding, most often whilst you are sleeping.

Can I transmit them to other people?
Yes, if they are on your clothes, luggage or furniture they can easily be transmitted to other people.

Can I get rid of them if they are in my house or hotel room?
Yes, if the infestation is light then you can treat it yourself, but if the bed bugs are well established then you must contact a professional pest management service to eradicate the problem. If you discover them in your hotel room, then report it to reception at once and demand to be moved to another room.

Be *Bed Bug Aware* and prevent infestations spreading. This book is designed to help you to be more *Bed Bug Aware*.

> ■ READ THIS BOOK TO ANSWER THESE QUESTIONS IN DETAIL – AND MANY MORE!
>
> ■ LEARN HOW TO PREVENT BED BUGS BECOMING A PROBLEM IN YOUR HOME OR WHILE YOU ARE TRAVELLING.
>
> ■ LEARN HOW TO ERADICATE AN INFESTATION IF YOU ARE UNLUCKY ENOUGH TO HAVE ONE IN YOUR HOME.

 Introduction

The resurgence of bed bugs has caught many people unawares. What used to be a subject of nursery rhymes is becoming a nightmare for many. Complaints about bed bugs have increased dramatically all over the world in the last few years. They should not be viewed as a problem associated with poverty or lack of good basic hygiene, but one that can affect us in all walks of life.

This guide is designed to help you to prevent them from infesting your home and to make the right decisions if they have already infested your home. It will tell you what to look for during your travels so that you avoid becoming a victim and, most importantly, avoid bringing them home to live with you!

This little book could save you months of anguish and money trying to get rid of bed bugs.

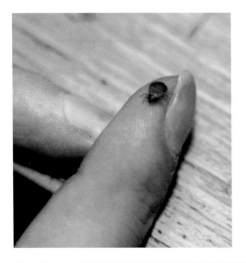

History

It is thought that bed bugs first associated themselves with humans during our cave dwelling era. They followed us out of the caves on our clothing of animal skins and have been a pest of both rural and urban living ever since. Bed bugs have been documented in literature as long ago as the 17th century. In his diaries, Samuel Pepys refers to bed bugs and measures to control them on several occasions.

Bed bugs were associated with the new city slums of the Industrial Revolution and on through Victorian times. We probably also transported them to far off lands as they were colonized.

During the 20th century the first attempts to document and understand the extent of the problem resulted in the estimate that, at one stage in the 1930's, 25% of all homes in the UK were infested!

Following World War II, the increased use of new synthetic insecticides such as DDT, helped to reduce their numbers greatly. This was complemented by improvements in health and hygiene associated with the move from poor city dwellings to the new suburban environments of the post war era.

The implementation of the Public Health Act in 1936, revised in 1961,

"Bed bugs on public transport spreading – The number of bed bugs found on public transport has risen dramatically in the past year."

Daily Telegraph Reporter, 26 August 2008

also did much to prevent the spread of bed bugs by making it an offence "to sell or re-sell verminous items" such as bedding and furniture.

Indeed until recently, bed bugs had ceased to be considered a significant pest in the UK or world wide.

The recent return

In the past two decades, bed bugs have made a comeback across the world. During the 1970's even pest control companies routinely servicing hotel accommodation in London would regard a bed bug problem as a rarity. One anecdotal signal that things were about to change came from an Environmental Health Officer who gave a regular presentation on pests on his local radio station during the mid 1980's. After each broadcast there were usually a handful of calls. Following a broadcast in which he talked about bed bugs, the radio station was deluged with calls.

Although bed bugs are not considered to be a health hazard they can be very unpleasant to live with. The rapid increase in international travel is often cited as a reason for the recent spread of bed bugs. This may be because all stages of the pest's life cycle, not just the adults, are readily transported in luggage, clothing, bedding and furniture. Bed bugs can infest aircraft, ships, trains and buses.

Bed bugs are most frequently found in locations with a high rate of occupancy change, such as hotels, hostels and apartment complexes. Such infestations are not usually a reflection of poor hygiene or bad housekeeping, but that a previous occupant had come into contact with bed bugs at some stage and left them behind for others to be bitten. As we all travel more, the chances of us confronting such a situation increases as does the likelihood that we, ourselves, become a vehicle to transport the bed bugs to our next hotel or our home.

Adult bed bugs are difficult to detect because their flat shape enables them to hide in the narrowest of cracks and crevices. In some cases insects have even been found in cracks where it would be difficult to insert a sheet of paper.

The young bed bugs are much more difficult to detect as they are often almost translucent. Bed bugs have now become global news. All over the world we can find newspaper horror stories and web postings about biting, infestation and transportation.

What are bed bugs?

Bed Bugs or *Cimex lectularius* and *Cimex hemipterus* are members of an insect order the Hemiptera. Although it is common nowadays to use the word "bug" as synonymous with the word insect, the Hemiptera are the "true bugs". There are over 80,000 species of Hemiptera which includes well known insects such as Aphids, Thrips and Whiteflies. Bed bugs are only a small family within this order called the Cimicidae.

Adult bed bugs are brown to reddish-brown, oval-shaped, flattened and about 5mm long. In size and shape they resemble a flattened ladybird. Their flat shape readily enables them to hide in cracks and crevices.

The most detectable signs of a bed bug infestation are:

- Being bitten by the bug.
- The presence of tell tale droppings called faecal traces.
- The presence of dead skins, live insects or tiny eggs.
- Blood spots on sheets.
- A faint sweet sickly smell which is not always detectable.

There is more information on bed bugs in the section on page 10 which looks at their biology, lifecycle and biting.

Why are they now spreading again?

Although there is no definitive reason for this global increase it is thought to be due to a number of factors:

■ The increase over the last decade of international travel.

■ An increase in short term occupancy of hotel rooms by business travellers, air crew and tourists.

■ The reduction in the use of residual insecticide treatments for cockroaches and other insect pests.

■ The re-use of infected furniture, particularly beds, mattresses and sofas, which should have been destroyed.

"Australian plague of bed bugs costs tourist industry millions – Travellers heading down under for a party-filled Christmas and New Year may be hoping to return with golden, sun-baked bodies – but they could just as easily end up with skin welts, itching patches and swollen bites."

The Independent, 6 November 2004

■ Resistance induced through ineffective treatments.

■ Undetected infestations where the person bitten has not had any detectable reaction to the bite.

■ Pest controllers losing the art of effective control as a result of bed bugs' comparative rarity for three decades.

A few years ago it was reported that almost every hotel in Sydney had signs of infestation following the 2000 Olympic Games, highlighting the fact that this is truly a global issue. It has recently been reported that because the Sydney issue was not immediately dealt with, the problem spread and now 75% of all hotels and short term accommodation in Australia has at least one infested room.

There is also increasing evidence that infestations in cities are spreading rapidly through transport corridors from inner city environments to suburban dwellings.

Life Cycle of the Bed Bug
Cimex lectularius

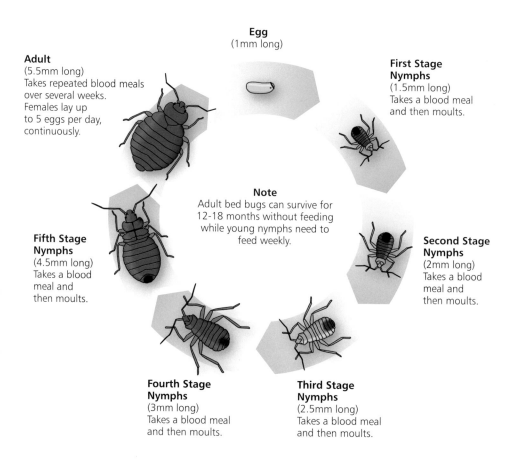

Egg
(1mm long)

Adult
(5.5mm long)
Takes repeated blood meals over several weeks. Females lay up to 5 eggs per day, continuously.

First Stage Nymphs
(1.5mm long)
Takes a blood meal and then moults.

Note
Adult bed bugs can survive for 12-18 months without feeding while young nymphs need to feed weekly.

Fifth Stage Nymphs
(4.5mm long)
Takes a blood meal and then moults.

Second Stage Nymphs
(2mm long)
Takes a blood meal and then moults.

Fourth Stage Nymphs
(3mm long)
Takes a blood meal and then moults.

Third Stage Nymphs
(2.5mm long)
Takes a blood meal and then moults.

The life cycle

Female bed bugs lay from one to twelve eggs per day, the eggs usually being deposited on rough surfaces or in cracks and crevices. The eggs are coated with a sticky substance so they can adhere to the surface on which they are laid.

Eggs hatch after approximately ten days, and the nymphs, which look like small skinny bed bugs, start to feed. They need a blood meal in order to shed their skin (moult) and develop into the next stage. Bed bugs moult five times before they mature into adults.

Feeding

To develop fully, bed bugs must take regular feeds of blood. They feed when people are stationary which means that they are usually most active at night while we rest, although they adapt easily to the feeding opportunities within their environment.

A blood meal can take only a few minutes to draw from the body and if disturbed while feeding they may move on to feed several times in a small area before returning to their hiding place to digest the meal. They may then emerge three or four days later to feed again.

Stegerphoto.com

A scanning electron micrograph of a bed bug head.

Bed bug bites and their implication for me

The first sign of a bed bug problem for most people is being bitten. The degree to which people respond to bed bug bites varies. For some people a bite may disappear within a matter of hours while others experience itching and inflammation for weeks.

Biting usually occurs whilst the victim (host) is sleeping. The bite is painless at the time but will typically cause the skin to become irritated and inflamed. In common with many other biting insects, bed bugs do not want to be detected while they are feeding otherwise they will come to a sticky end! They, therefore, inject a small amount of anaesthetic into the bite, together with an anticoagulant to prevent their 'meal' from clotting while they feed. It is this 'cocktail' that causes the inflammation.

Bed bug bites can be differentiated from other insect bites such as fleas, as consisting of a whitish swelling with no red puncture mark at the centre of the bite. Each bed bug may bite several times during one night, giving the appearance that an infestation is much worse than it really is. Individuals differ greatly in both the extent and timing of their response to a bite.

A small, hard, swollen, white welt may develop at the site of each bite. These can occur in rows or batches of three or four. This is accompanied by severe itching that lasts from several hours to days. In rare cases an allergic reaction may follow - in such cases medical attention should be sought immediately.

It is believed that one in ten people show no signs of biting, often leading to the myth that they only attack certain people. It is believed that six out of ten people do not initially respond to a bite, but may eventually do so as the numbers of bed bugs and bites increase. Cases of extreme reaction may affect as many as two in ten people. People who exhibit a severe reaction to other insect bites, such as fleas and mosquitoes, are more likely to have an extreme reaction to bed bugs.

There is also increasing anecdotal evidence that the environment in which an infestation occurs may affect the severity of any reaction to bites by the victim. Areas of high pollution may increase the likelihood of external irritants entering the wound caused by the bite and inducing a more severe reaction.

Beware!

The appearance of bites is highly variable and bed bugs are almost impossible to diagnose through bites alone. We have deliberately not included images of bites because they are not definitive signs of an infestation. A qualified medical person, such as a doctor should be consulted if itching or inflammation persists and the other definite signs of an infestation are not present.

How and where might I get exposed?

Bed bugs can spread from any area where people spend a long enough time for bed bugs to infest clothing or luggage. They tend to be most associated with bedroom furniture and hotel rooms but they could be found literally anywhere there are the right conditions.

Over recent years infestations have been reported in the following places:

- Domestic properties – houses, apartments and mobile homes.

- Hotels – all grades from bed & breakfast to five star properties.

- All types of public transport – trains, mass transit systems, buses and coaches.

- Cinemas and theatres.

- Offices.

- Restaurants.

- Shops.

- Commercial and private transport vehicles – cars and vans.

- Aircraft.

- Hostels –backpacker and sheltered housing.

- Prisons.

- Oil Rigs.

The simple fact is that they can be found anywhere that people visit or occupy. That is not to say that all of these places are all infested all of the time but it does illustrate that there could be a problem.

The greater the level of infestation and the longer you spend in an infested location, the greater the chance that they will hitch a ride out of that location with you.

Yes they can spread that easily!!!

Are there any health concerns?

Relax – There are no known links between bed bugs and disease transmission despite extensive research in this area. Although undoubtedly one of the more annoying and nuisance pests, especially if you react to the bites, they do not pose a direct threat to your health.

How do I tell if a bite is from a bed bug?

First of all it is important to understand that there are many insects that bite, especially if you are travelling. The presence of bites does not automatically mean you have been exposed to bed bugs!!

If you do not see any of the distinctive signs of a bed bug infestation listed on the next page then it is possible that you may have a problem relating to another insect. Remember that most insects inject an anaesthetic when they bite so you may not be aware that you have been bitten until sometime afterwards.

Some other common insects that bite are:

Carpet beetles – A relatively common problem in centrally heated houses. Although carpet beetles do not bite the hairs on the larval stage can cause a bite like reaction with some people.

Fleas – especially if you have cats and dogs as pets.

Scabies or lice – easily passed from close contact with already infected people but signs may take up to a month to show after initial exposure.

Dust mites – increasingly associated with asthma.

Bird mites – from birds nesting in the eaves, gutters, outbuildings or garages.

As a guide to identifying what could be biting you we suggest the following:

- Make a thorough inspection of any area where you think you may have been bitten, for example the bedroom, hotel room or sofa. Look for any signs of live or dead insects, anything that could be small eggs or larvae. If they look like very small caterpillars, then the problem is not bed bugs.

- Check the walls, ceiling, curtains and bathroom for mosquitoes.

- If the bites are mainly between the fingers, arm pits or groin area consult a medical professional, this may be the signs of a scabies infection not bed bug bites.

- If the bites are mainly on the ankles or the lower part of the legs, it is very likely that fleas are the cause. Buy and use a plug-in flea trap similar to the trap pictured on this page, to monitor for the presence of fleas. www.PestFreeHome.co.uk always has flea traps in stock.

- Inspect loft spaces and external walls for signs of birds' nesting areas which could be indicative of either bird mites or carpet beetles.

Finally, below is a good web link to an article that explains causes of itching, both from insect bites and other sources of potential irritation.
http://www.ca.uky.edu/agc/pubs/ent/ent58/ent58.pdf

Plug in flea trap

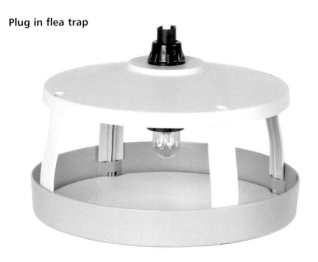

Picture courtesy of STV Ltd.

"Edinburgh hit by plague of bed bugs –

Edinburgh is facing a new battle – against a massive bed bug invasion. Pest controllers are getting six times as many calls about the bloodsuckers as they did a year ago..."

Daily Record, 8 October 2008

How can I confirm if I have bed bugs in my home?

Detection

A thorough inspection of the room or house is necessary to locate bed bugs and the places where they will hide, which are called their "harbourages".

You are looking for the physical indications explained below. Inspection should centre first in the bedroom and particularly the bed itself. Firstly check both sides of the mattress, concentrating particularly on the piping around the edges and any buttoning in the mattress. Next check the bed-frame, making sure to look underneath to check the box springs. Seek out and check the cracks and crevices that the bed bugs may hide in during the day or when digesting their meal of human blood.

Next, being equally thorough, check the headboard and bed side tables.

After this, check the window and door frames, floor cracks, carpet fixing boards at the edges of the room, skirting boards, electrical sockets, other furniture, pictures, wall hangings, curtain pleats, loosened wallpaper, cracks in plaster and ceiling mouldings.

If you find bed bugs, elimination of an infestation will require thorough cleaning and any insecticide treatments to be focused correctly. In most cases this is a job for a specialist professional company such as www.bed-bugs.co.uk. Later in the book we explain how and when you could treat an infestation yourself and when you should call in a specialist professional company.

Physical indications of bed bug infestations

The physical indicators you should be looking for are:

Faecal traces

These are the minute droppings of the bed bug and these marks are very much unique to bed bugs. The bigger the infestation, the greater the number of these marks that will be present. One of the best tests to determine if a mark is due to bed bugs is to attempt to smear it with a little moisture. Marks due to bed bug faeces will streak when liquid is applied. The marks will generally be found close to the nesting area of the bed bugs.

Live bed bugs

One of the common misconceptions about bed bugs is that they are too small to see. As the pictures throughout this book illustrate, that is not true. Although small, they can be detected by the human eye although a magnifying lens may help you to verify your identification. An adult bed

bug can lay between 150 and 300 eggs, so they can move rapidly to colonise new areas. Usually by the second or third month of an infestation they are breeding at a very fast rate making their presence easy to detect.

Old cast off skins

Bed bug skins often resemble a paper thin and slightly opaque version of a bed bug. When skins are found, live bed bugs are usually close by.

Blood spots on sheets

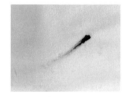

A bed bug infestation may be recognized by blood stains from crushed bugs or by rusty (sometimes dark) spots of excrement on sheets and mattresses, bed clothes and walls. This sign, however, is not always present and on sheets this may be due to a nick or cut on the skin. If you find spots on the sheets check the corresponding part of your body for signs of cuts or grazes before assuming it is bed bugs. This, along with the bites, is often the first sign you will encounter in a hotel room.

Sweet sickly smell

Some people can detect a sweet sickly smell when an infestation of bed bugs is present. This does take a while to build up, is usually associated with a heavy infestation and you may not be aware of it if you are a regular occupant of the room.

How do I make sure I don't get bed bugs in my home?

It is so much easier to establish a routine to make sure that your home does not get infested, than it is to get rid of any infestation, however small, once it is established.

Prevention

Identifying the potential source is one of the key factors to controlling any infestation. The aim must be to ensure that no potential source of bed bugs is brought into the home.

Any item that could be infested should not be brought into the home, until it has been thoroughly checked. This includes second hand furniture, beds, bedding or furnishings which may be acquired for the home. Having checked them, if you think they might be infested, do not bring them into the home or at least treat them with a non-pesticide product such as diatomaceous earth first. This product, together with an applicator, is available as a complete bed bug treatment kit from www.PestFreeHome.co.uk.

Luggage and clothing of family members or visitors, who have been travelling, should be inspected carefully for actual bed bugs or any of the signs described on the previous page. If there are any bed bugs or signs of their activity then items can be treated with a bed bug kit or decontaminated by the 'Out of Home' bed bug decontamination services offered exclusively by Bed Bugs UK and www.PestFreeHome.co.uk.

Good hygiene

Good hygiene practices are essential to keep your home free of bed bugs. These include frequent vacuuming of the mattresses and carpets throughout the house. If you are concerned about bed bug infestations then use a stiff brush to "scrub" the mattress seams to dislodge bed bugs and eggs before vacuuming. After vacuuming, immediately place the contents of the vacuum cleaner in a plastic bag, seal tightly, and discard in the outdoor waste bin. This prevents captured bed bugs from escaping back into your home and spreading from room to room.

Discarding old or potentially infested mattresses is another option, although a new mattress can quickly become infested if bed bugs are still in the house.

If you or your family travel frequently or you have a lot of visitors then it is wise to establish a routine of monthly inspections alongside a thorough cleaning process. This will minimize the chances of infestation occurring in the first place or becoming established.

How do I check if I have bed bugs?

On the previous pages we have explained the physical evidence that may lead you to think that you have a bed bug infestation, such as being bitten or finding blood spots on sheets.

In addition we have described where to look for live bed bugs. There are however, other ways to check.

Using bed bug monitors

Recent scientific advances have led to a range of bed bug monitoring devices now being available. They are broadly grouped into two types; active and passive. Both work in different ways and have different roles in the detection and control of bed bugs.

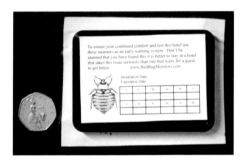

Passive monitors

The concept and design of passive bed bug monitors was developed as a tool to help those worried about being exposed to bed bugs and wanting a system for early detection.

Once installed they remain effective for up to a year to detect the tell tale signs of bed bugs. The "Passive Monitors" can be placed discreetly in areas where bed bugs might live or move. For best results they need to be checked regularly – at least monthly.

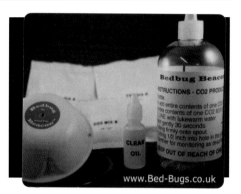

www.Bed-Bugs.co.uk

Active monitors and traps

In addition to these "passive" monitors there are now effective "active" monitors that can be used to attract and trap bed bugs. Active monitors are expensive and usually only used to confirm that live bed bugs are present.

If any indication that bed bugs are present is found, a confirmation can then be made using an active monitor within 24 hours.

Using dog detection systems

One very new way of detecting the presence of bed bugs is the use of specially trained "sniffer" dogs. These are called "K9 Teams". The ability of dogs to detect and differentiate between the molecules of different chemicals at low concentrations and therefore to detect bed bugs, still far exceeds that of the best analytical equipment yet devised.

Through extensive training, the dogs and their handlers can act as a team to detect and confirm infestations rapidly and accurately. Most US cities now have a dedicated dog and handler team. At the time of publication there is only one "K9 team" working in the UK. We expect to see a lot more teams in the near future.

Disposing of infested items such as old mattresses or sofas can present a problem. Unless carefully managed you run the risk of spreading the infestation through the rest of your property making the eradication of bed bugs even more difficult.

When removing items from your home you are advised to take the following precautions.

Wrap and seal the items while they are still in the infested room. Moving them could spread the problem. If the items are small then food storage film is good enough, but if the item is large then use polythene sheeting to ensure that the item is 100% contained and there is no risk of spreading the bed bugs further

Remove the wrapped and sealed items straight to the outside for disposal.

If you own or manage a hotel, guest house or hostel and you are storing or leaving the wrapped items temporarily in a public access area for any length of time, it is important to identify the package as "Infested". Use the Bed Bug Beware image below to ensure that others do not take the infestation into their homes. This image can also be accessed in full resolution and printed free of charge from: www.bedbugbeware.com/cautionnote.jpg

Many professional pest controllers will be able to advise you how to dispose of infested items or will take them away themselves for safe disposal. Alternatively contact your local council to find out what services they may offer.

Under no circumstances consider selling or donating any infested items for further use, especially to second hand shops. This will only contribute to making the overall bed bug situation in your area worse.

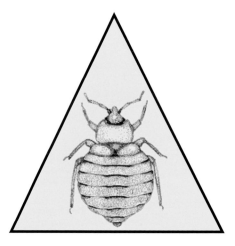

Should I treat the bed bugs myself or call in a professional service?

Once you have confirmed that you have bed bugs in your home the next decision is how best to treat the infestation.

There is a lot you can do to identify the source and extent of the problem. This will help you decide whether the infestation is light enough for you to be able to treat yourself or if you need professional advice or treatment.

The first step in clearing an infestation is to identify the source and understand the extent of the problem. Carefully and thoroughly check all rooms for signs of bed bug activity. Avoid moving or disposing of items from any room as too much disturbance may spread the infestation to adjoining rooms.

Avoid moving furniture and bedding between rooms and, where possible, clothes that are not being used should be washed at a temperature above 60°C and sealed in plastic bags. Any beds should be left in their usual place but special care should be taken to ensure that the area around and under affected beds is kept free and clear.

It is important not to dispose of any furniture until it has been treated. Replacing the bed may give a respite for a few days but the problem will return.

What you can do if the infestation is low

Only if the infestation is light should you attempt to treat the problem yourself. From experience we would suggest that a light infestation is when:

there are no more than 20 live insects found per room;
or
there are no more than 40 faecal traces found per room;
and
when the infestation detected is in less than one third of the rooms in the house.

In the section "Doing It Yourself" we give some useful tips about what products to use, what not to use and how to get the best from them.

Caution

Do not treat the problem yourself more than three times. If by this time you have not controlled the bed bug infestation then stop and call in an experienced professional.

What should you do if the infestation is severe or you are not sure?

You should either call a professional bed bug control company such as Bed-Bugs UK or your local council.

A dozen things not to do

Once you have decided that you have a light enough infestation to treat yourself or you have arranged for your local council or a professional bed bug treatment company to treat the infestation, there are a few key things that you must not do if you want to ensure the best chance to eradicate the problem.

> If in any doubt call a professional bed bug control service such as www.bed-bugs.co.uk or your local council.

These include:

- Do not move furniture and bedding between rooms.

- Do not dispose of any furniture until it has been treated.

- Do not replace the bed.

- Do not move clothes out of the infested room.

Fox News worker sues over bed bugs in NY office – NEW YORK (Reuters) –

A Fox News employee who says she suffers from post traumatic stress disorder after being bitten by bed bugs at work filed a lawsuit on Thursday..."

Reuters Business and Finance, 29 May 2008

If you are treating a light infestation yourself then:

- Do not use any fogging systems, such as smoke canisters, to treat the problem.

- Do not use any aerosols to treat the problem.

- Do not use any products marked "flammable".

- Do not try in any way to raise the temperature as a heat treatment.

- Do not use any products marked "For Professional Use Only".

- Do not use insecticide baits.

- Do not assume that more is better when it comes to insecticides as the overuse of products can cause more problems within your home.

- **Do not panic**, read the product label carefully and any practical tips that specialist websites, such as www.PestFreeHome.co.uk, provide before application.

"Bloodthirsty bed bugs are back... thanks to global warming! – Watch out! 'Global warming' is causing an invasion of bed bugs in our homes."

East London Advertiser, 29 October 2007

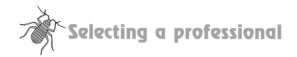
Finding out you have an infestation of bed bugs can be an unpleasant experience and eradicating them quickly and efficiently is most likely your highest priority.

Selecting the right professional and expert company to help you with your bed bug problem is just like selecting any other service option for your home.

It is important that the company you choose is qualified and experienced and has the appropriate information to reassure you of this. Hiring the cheapest company may or may not turn out to be a prudent choice. It is important to be able to decide between a professional business and a potential "cowboy". Below we list some advice to assist your decision

Check with Companies House (www.companieshouse.gov.uk) through their "Search Company Information" web check service. This will reassure you that the company you are looking up is registered as a legal limited company.

Make sure the business you contact is experienced in dealing with bed bugs. Bed bugs are a problematic pest at the best of times and without experience, it is possible to spread them around the property. Just telling you that they can treat rats, mice, flies, fleas and cockroaches is not experience in treating bed bugs!

Make sure that the business and the technician they send is dealing with a significant enough number of bed bug cases each week. Ideally a minimum of six to eight per week in urban areas. Experience outside of urban areas can be a

lot harder to find.

If you are told that you need to dispose of all furniture from the infested rooms without inspecting your premises, the business clearly does not understand how bed bugs live and breed and may not be experienced enough to resolve your problem. Make sure that the business carries public and product liability insurance to carry out the work at your property. You can check what the minimum is by contacting the British Pest Control Association whose members must carry a minimum level of cover.

"Tenant claims block of flats is riddled with bed bugs – A tenant at a council flat in Barton Hill claims a whole tower block has become infested with bed bugs."

Bristol Evening Post, 16 August 2008

Checking with the national trade association for professional pest controllers can be a good place to start (www.bpca.org.uk or www.npta.org.uk). The BPCA has a post code search facility on its website. Do not assume that because the business is a member, that it is experienced in dealing with bed bugs.

When discussing treatment options ask about what you need to do before they start (pre-treatment) and after they finish (post-treatment). Your own activity plays an important part in getting the best results

"**Lawyer bitten by bed bugs sues leading London hotel** – A New York lawyer is suing a leading London hotel after he and his wife were attacked by bed bugs."

"****** ******* and his wife ******* are seeking several million dollars in damages"

Daily Mail, 17 January 2007

from their treatment. Ask about the health and safety aspects of the treatments that they are applying. Ask them for a "Material Safety Data Sheet" (MSDS) for all products that the business proposes to use. Businesses are obliged to provide a MSDS if requested. Professional companies are rarely too busy to let you know what they are doing and to make sure that you are fully briefed.

The products that professional pest controllers usually use are approved by government legislation for use only by professionals. They must not supply the customer with these products for their own use. If they do, or if they suggest you "buy something from the internet", it is

questionable whether they really do have the necessary experience.

Removal of bed bugs requires co-operation between the professionals and yourself, if you do not get the feeling that the service being offered is comprehensive it may not yield the effective results you are expecting.

There are no miracle, overnight, solutions to bed bug problems. If the company makes miracle promises then they are unlikely to be able to deliver them.

If the pest controller proposes to use an insecticide bait, find another business. No insecticide bait currently on the market is approved for, or will be effective against, bed bugs.

Doing it yourself

There is currently no fully effective home treatment solution, although certain house keeping activities will help reduce infestations.

After checking the information on page 21 to help you assess the severity of the infestation, you may consider the infestation light enough to treat yourself. Be aware that no guarantees of complete control will be given on any of the products that you purchase. Success will be dependent on the accuracy of your assessment of the severity, the scale of the infestation and on the diligence with which you apply the selected product.

Choosing the right product

To be effective the insecticide needs to be 'residual' (it continues to remain toxic to bed bugs for several days after it has been applied). Most aerosol fly-sprays will not offer this necessary longevity. The insecticide must also be in a form that will provide a layer that the bed bugs will walk across. This means that the 'active' part of the insecticide must not be absorbed into the surfaces to which it is being applied and the product must not be detectable and repellent to the bed bugs.

As explained above, bed bugs are only interested in feeding on you. Bed bugs will not be attracted to baits so don't be tempted to purchase a bait based remedy!

Having selected the correct product and remembering that it will be one that stays on the surface to which it is applied, avoid over diligent use of the vacuum cleaner, otherwise you will quickly remove the protection that you have, so carefully, put in place.

Diatomaceous earth

The only currently available products that Bed Bugs UK and PestFreeHome.co.uk would advise you to consider are dusts based on diatomaceous earth. Such products are available from www.PestFreeHome.co.uk either separately or combined with a dust applicator in our simple and easy to use bed bug kit. Diatomaceous earth meets all of the criteria listed previously and kills bed bugs by damaging the waxy layer of the insect's cuticle (its shell). Insects are dependent upon this "shell" to retain water. Once damaged they quickly dry up (dehydrate) and die.

Treating with a mini duster

Look for joints in beds, bedside furniture and bedroom fittings; under dado and picture rails; beneath the edges of wallpaper. Check the mattress particularly the piping around the edge and under the buttoning. Carefully apply the dust to the "cracks and crevices" in the walls, the joints in the bed and the headboard. Anywhere the bed bugs may be hiding. Also treat along the edges of the mattress and into the button holes.

If you do treat the mattress, leave the dust in place for three days and then vacuum up the dust.

Further actions you can take after treating the infestation

Once you have treated the infestation you may want to take additional steps to 'isolate' yourself and your family from further potential bites. One way to do this is to install mattress covers onto each mattress in the house and to put passive bed bug monitors in place. The monitors will give you early warning of a recurrence of the problem, whilst the mattress covers will provide a barrier between yourself and the bed bugs whilst additional control measures are taken.

If you find that you have a bed bug infestation in your personal items, especially in stored clothing, storage drawers, a small suitcase, cabin bag or rucksack it can be difficult to get rid of the infestation. This is an increasing problem, but now with an innovative solution.

Bed Bugs UK has set up a specialist decontamination process away from your home called the Off Site Decon™ service which can be purchased on line through PestFreeHome.co.uk. The pack supplied to you includes a sealable storage bag, courier box, packaging material and instructions outlining exactly how items for decontamination need to be packed to ensure that there is no contamination during transport.

The sealed package is collected, decontaminated with our complete pesticide free service and returned to your home. The decontamination process takes between 14 and 18 days for most items and ensures complete eradication of the bed bugs and their eggs. At this time this service is not suitable for electronic items or photographic materials. Detailed instructions on what can be decontaminated are included in the decontamination pack.

The service is discrete and confidential and with no need to break the seal on the package.

How do I avoid bed bugs when I am travelling?

One of the principal reasons for the increase in incidence of bed bugs is increased travel. If your hotel room has an infestation of bed bugs they can easily spread to your luggage and clothes and hitch a ride home with you. The risk of picking up a couple of unwanted travelling companions is much the same regardless of whether you are staying in a five star hotel, a hostel or even on a friend's sofa bed!

Travellers should if possible, seal their luggage with a protective layer of cling film or pallet wrap during long haul flights – this is to avoid picking up bed bugs from adjoining bags in the cargo hold. Although this is a small risk and one of the less frequent methods of transmission, as bed bug problems increase globally it is likely to become more common. Don't help bed bugs to spread.

Many travel websites offer reviews on all aspects of hotels through "customer experience" message boards. A quick check on accommodation you are considering can often reveal if any previous clients have included bed bug problems amongst their comments.

How to inspect a hotel room

Before unpacking your bags just a quick three minute check of the room for signs of bed bugs can save days of discomfort.

Always check the bed and surrounding furniture for the following signs:

- Clusters of eggs and live insects around the head board especially near joints in the wood and behind any pictures that hang above the bed.

- Signs of excreted blood near the junction of the wooden slats and bed frame.

- Signs of live insects or excreted blood on the mattress most commonly on the darker side or against a wall. Also check the mattress piping on the edges and corners and the buttoning.

If you are in doubt about a room request a change to another part of the accommodation. A sensible host or hotelier will be aware that rapid identification and treatment is the only solution for the effective eradication of bed bugs. Even if the room appears clear never place your bag under the bed. In the earliest stages of an infestation visible evidence may be scarce and the insects are most likely to be in the same area that they were deposited in, often from the previous occupant's bag.

A final tip

Upon arrival at your next destination, take the time to unpack and inspect all your items to ensure that no unwanted hitchhikers have come along for the ride.

What to do if you become exposed to bed bugs during your travels?

Early detection and identification of the source are the most important issues in successfully controlling and eradicating bed bugs. If you do not discuss your experiences with the owner of the room you picked up the bed bugs from, they may not be aware of the problem – after all not everybody gets bitten. By bringing it to their attention you will be helping fellow travellers and helping to prevent the spread of bed bugs.

What to do if you find bed bugs

If you become aware that you have been exposed to bed bugs while travelling, it is important that you take the following steps as quickly as possible before you move on to your next or home location. Remember bed bugs can easily hitchhike from location to location. If you do not deal with the problem before returning to your property they may follow you there.

In the event that you have been exposed and notice either bites or unexplained blood spots on the sheet on your bed, take time out of your schedule to perform the following steps prior to checking into your next destination:

- Open your bag and repack all items, sorted into washable loads sealed in laundry bags. You can now buy special bags that will dissolve in the washing machine.
- Examine the bag including all seams, zips and pockets for signs of bed bugs. If any eggs or live insects are found the bag should be sealed in a refuse bag and disposed of. Alternatively scrub manually with very hot water to remove and destroy the insects.
- Purchase a new outfit, change into it and visit a laundrette to wash all your clothes. All items should either be thoroughly inspected for signs of bed bugs or washed at a minimum temperature of 60°C.
- Items that are not washable such as books and electronic equipment should be inspected and if in doubt left sealed in a refuse bag until they can be professionally treated.

If it is not feasible for you to process the infested items then they MUST be sealed and remain that way until you can make arrangements for their treatment. Dry cleaning processes will not always kill bed bugs and are not a recognized method of decontamination.

Many professional pest controllers and bed bug specialists are now offering specialist services to manage this decontamination process. Check at either bed-bugs.co.uk or PestFreeHome.co.uk for this service.

"Mind the bed bugs don't bite as critter numbers boom – Be warned – next time you return from a foreign jaunt, you might have brought back a very unwelcome souvenir."

thisislondon.co.uk, 19 October 2006

What are the scientists doing to help us?

As we have described in this book, bed bugs have become a resurgent problem worldwide over the last few years. The precise reason for this is unknown but it is likely to have something to do with changing travel habits and our own transient urban lifestyle.

As a result it is only in the last few years that scientists and specialist pest control technical managers have started to look anew at the problem of bed bugs.

Although scientists and entomologists are increasing their interest and activity in the prevention and control of bed bugs, most of the innovative science and ground breaking ideas are coming from practical field technicians that are specializing in the control of bed bugs.

The major areas that scientists are looking at are:

■ Technology to ensure earlier detection of bed bugs. The first bed bug monitoring devices are only now becoming available. These technologies will allow early detection of bed bugs ensuring that infestations do not develop to an extent that they become a risk to others by accident and through lack of awareness.

■ Specialist scent detection units are starting to become more widely available. Although extensively available in the US for some time, quarantine and animal transport restrictions prohibited earlier introduction to the UK. It can be expected that trained "K9 units" will become more

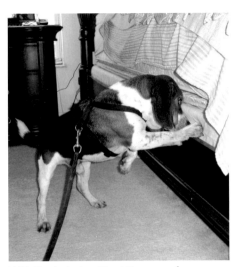

With thanks to Jose 'Pepe' Peruyero of J & K Canine Academy, High Springs, Florida, USA for the use of the photo.

available in the next few years and will be used increasingly in the investigation and assessment of large areas or multiple room hotels.

■ New chemicals and formulations to control bed bugs are being researched and developed. Due to the high levels of regulatory control and testing needed before a product can be permitted to be sold, it can be expected that these developments will take time before they are commercially available. We need to rely upon the products and tools that we have today for some time yet.

■ Many entomologists are studying the detailed biology and biochemical makeup of bed bugs. It is hoped that we can be more effective in controlling bed bugs if we understand them at a cellular level. Just as it can take years for a medical breakthrough to be translated into a cure, it will take time for us to be able to harness this important scientific information into more efficient treatment options.

■ Having studied the problem of bed bugs from a scientific perspective extensively over recent years, we conclude that the only effective way to control the spread of bed bugs is to communicate the need for people to be bed bug aware both in their own homes and when they are travelling.

Further sources of information

The following is a selection of links to sites which contain accurate and valuable information about the removal and control of bed bugs.

Inclusion of links is in no way an endorsement of their products or services by the authors.

Web sites

www.bed-bugs.co.uk
Britain's best known and most comprehensive professional bed bug prevention and control service. Based in London and managed by one of the authors – David Cain, Bed-Bugs UK has been providing extensive information since June 2005. David and his team ONLY treat bed bugs and have made over 10,000 inspections and treatments in the last four years.

www.PestFreeHome.co.uk
A specialist website providing solutions to bed bugs and other pest problems in the UK. PestFreeHome.co.uk offers the most comprehensive service to the home owner that includes an insect identification service, natural products and solutions. With every product additional advice is included from our experts, whch include this book's authors.

    PestFreeHome.co.uk offers a range of bed bug prevention and control options that link with those used and recommended by Bed-Bugs UK

www.bedbugbeware.com
BedBugBeware is an open access site with excellent advice and information on the detection and avoidance of bed bugs. Many of the pictures and advice in this book are included on the site. You can download and print the Bed Bug Beware Triangle.

www.bedbugcentral.com
Bed Bug Central is an educational website powered by knowledgeable pest control experts and pest control professionals in the US who recognized the need for a reliable and factual bed bug resource on the web. The goal of Bed Bug Central is to provide US consumers with current and accurate information and news about bed bugs, as well as to offer useful product recommendations.

www.uky.edu/Ag/Entomology/entfacts/struct/ef636.htm
Information from Professor Michael F Potter, extension entomologist University of Kentucky USA. Professor Potter's group have conducted some of the leading bed bug research including extensive resistance studies.

www.bedbugger.com
Information site and active forum for people suffering from bed bug related issues. Although mainly US focused they welcome people from all over the world.

www.bedbug.org.au
Department of Medical Entomology, ICPMR, Westmead Hospital Australia, Bed Bug web site run by Professor Doggett, one of the world's bed bug specialists.

www.bedbugresource.com
Information site and forum run by Sean Rollo entomologist and pest controller. Sean is one of the leading lights in bed bug control and a fountain of knowledge in Canada.

http://en.wikipedia.org/wiki/Bedbug
Wikipedia entry about bed bugs. It is a good place to start learning about bed bugs.

http://www.uos.harvard.edu/bed bugs/
Harvard University, information on the identification and biology of bed bugs.

References/Further reading

Larry Pinto, Richard Cooper, Sandy Kraft. *Bed Bug Handbook: The Complete Guide to Bed Bugs and Their Control*. Mechanicsville, Maryland: Pinto & Associates, December 2007.
ISBN 978-0-9788878-1-0

Forsyth, Adrian. *Die Sexualität in der Natur. Vom Egoismus der Gene und ihren unfeinen Strategien.* Munich: Deutscher Taschenbuch Verlag, 1991.
ISBN 3-423-11331-6

Forsyth, Adrian. *A Natural History of Sex: The Ecology and Evolution of Mating Behavior.* Richmond Hill, Ontario: Firefly Books, 2001.
ISBN 1-55209-481-2

Goddard, Jerome A. *The Physician's Guide to Arthropods of Medical Importance* (second edition). Boca Raton, Florida: CRC Press, 1993.
ISBN 0-8493-5160-X

MacQuitty, Miranda, and Lawrence Mound. *Megabugs: The Natural History Museum Book of Insects.* New York: Random House Children's Books, 1995.
ISBN 1-898304-37-8
ISBN 1-85868-045-X

Quammen, David. *The Flight of the Iguana: A Sidelong View of Science and Nature.* New York: Delacorte Press, 1988.
ISBN 0-385-29592-8
ISBN 0-385-26327-9
ISBN 0-684-83626-2
Provides detail about *Xylocaris maculipennis*.

Martin Leverkus, Ryan C. Jochim, Susanne Schad *et al. Bullous allergic hypersensitivity to bed bug bites mediated by IgE against Salivary nitrophorin.* J. Invest. Dermatol. (2006) 126, 91-96.

Glossary of technical terms

Cimicidae	The insect family to which the bed bugs belong.
DDT	Dichloro-diphenyl-trichloroethane. The first widely available synthetic Insecticide, used for many years for the control of insects. It is very persistent, accumulating in animals high up the food chain. It is now no longer registered for use in many countries.
Decon System™	A specialist "Out of Home" system for eradicating bed bugs without damage to the treated material.
Diatomaceous Earth	A natural organic product for controlling insects, which is ground from a sedimentary rock called Diatomite. It kills insects by damaging their cuticle (shell). The insect dies from dehydration rather than by poisoning.
Entomologist	A person who is qualified in the study of insects.
Faecal traces	The visible remains of the excrement of bed bugs.
Harbourage	Place of refuge for bed bugs, often in cracks or crevices.
Hecatombs	Ancient word for massacre or large scale slaughter.
Hemiptera	The insect order to which the Cimicidae belong. Commonly known as the "true bugs".
Infestation	The presence of a significant number of pests such as bed bugs in a single location.
Insect Cuticle	The outer layer of the skin of many invertebrate animals such as bed bugs.
Insect Family	A sub division of the 'insect order', used in insect classification to group a number of different species with similar features.
Insect Order	A way of classifying insects into large closely related groups such as the Hemiptera, the order which contains bed bugs. There are some 29 orders of insects covering over a million different species.
"K 9" Units	Specially trained dogs and their handlers which can seek out bed bug infestations.
Life Cycle	The progression through a number of differing stages of development when an insect passes from egg to adult.
Nymph	The immature form of an insect that resembles the adult, but is smaller and is not sexually mature.
Residual Insecticide	An insecticide that continues to remain toxic to insects, such as bed bugs for several days after it has been applied.
Resistance	An adaptation of an insect population decreasing susceptibility to a specific chemical to the extent that a sufficient proportion of that population survives to maintain the population.
Synthetic Insecticide	An insecticide made through an industrial process.
Verminous	Description of various small animals or insects that are destructive, annoying or injurious to health.

THE HILL-FORTS of PICTLAND

since
'The Problem of the Picts'

CW00928356

Ian Ralston

ISBN 0-9540999-1-5

Acknowledgements:

I would like to thank Susan Seright for the invitation to present this
material in a lecture at Groam House Museum, and Dr Graham Ritchie
for standing in for me at very short notice when health problems prevented
me from delivering it at the first attempt. This written version has bene-
fited from comments, advice and indications of other pertinent literature
from Professor James Graham-Campbell (University College, London),
Drs Ewan Campbell and Stephen Driscoll (Glasgow University), Dr John
Smith (Aberdeen University), Ian Shepherd (Aberdeenshire Council),
Derek Alexander (National Trust for Scotland) and Melanie Johnson,
Andrew Dunwell and Bruce Glendinning of CFA Archaeology Ltd
(Musselburgh). I am grateful to Eleanor Wilkinson for her draughts-
manship, and to Jim Livingston and Ian Shepherd for help with photo-
graphs. Final responsibility for the form and content of this essay however
rests solely with the author.

Ian Ralston, Pennygown, Mull, 2003

Introduction

This paper is an attempt to take stock of aspects of the secular enclosed sites of Pictland – hill-forts in standard archaeological jargon. The geographical focus will be primarily on its mainland component, more particularly on the country to the south and east of Inverness. This comprises the area that is sometimes referred to as the Pictish heartland. Indisputable examples of such sites are in any case still rare in the north mainland and on Scotland's off-shore islands. A secondary geographical theme will involve consideration of regional differentiation within Pictland, and indeed more generally across Scotland. Richard Feachem reviewed the evidence then available in his important contribution to the seminal series of papers delivered at Dundee to the Scottish Summer School in Archaeology in August 1952. Subsequently published in *The Problem of the Picts* in 1955 (Wainwright 1955), that article forms the springboard for the present exercise.

Hill- and promontory forts and other enclosed sites

Most of the sites to be considered have been described as either hill- or promontory-forts. For present purposes, the term 'hill-fort' will be used in a broad and inclusive way (cf. Shaw and Jamieson 1999, 278) and without prejudice as to the assumed function or functions of these sites. Ecclesiastical sites enclosed by a *vallum* or by similar arrangements, like that at Portmahomack, Easter Ross, presently being examined by Professor Martin Carver (e.g. Carver 2001), are however excluded. The use of the term 'hill-fort' in a general sense here should be taken to embrace promontory forts, as well as those located on summits of whatever form.

Slighter consideration will also be given to suites of smaller sites (including those conventionally known as duns and/or ring-forts), because in the 1950s they were considered essentially as defensive structures and thus fell within Feachem's remit. In their case, however, there is now good evidence for envisaging that some, potentially many, such sites – in Pictland and beyond – were actually substantial roofed buildings rather than fortified enclosures with free-standing internal structures (e.g. for early examples: Hingley *et al.* 1997; more generally Harding 1984; 1997, 123; for Atholl, Taylor 1990). Such sites were clearly already being constructed within the pre-Roman Iron Age, although others are attributable to the first millennium AD. In this study, however, the writer will steer clear of the important later accretions constructed within and surrounding complex Atlantic roundhouses, the sites standardly described as brochs. The re-use of such sites is a well-recognised component of the settlement record of Atlantic Scotland in the first millennium AD (Alcock 1984; Foster 1997; Harding and Gilmour 2000), but they are very different in character from the hill-forts of the same period, and do not appear to have been defensive in primary intent.

Dating and problems of definition

As regards chronological range, consideration will be given to sites with broadly first millennium AD evidence from the appropriate geographical area, rather than to the narrower definitions of 'Pictish' as a period division that are advocated by some authors (varying practice in this regard is usefully reviewed by Foster 1997, 6). This admittedly slackly-defined chronological bracket offers scope for setting the sites examined in wider context, and at least implicitly acknowledges some of the imprecision as to exact date-spans inherent in the radiocarbon determinations that will be pressed into service.[1]

This essay should thus be regarded as a partial auditing exercise, undertaken at a distinctly basic level, and that from a substantially archaeological perspective. It makes no pretence to be a complete inventory of possible, probable and certain Pictish forts. Without quantifying that task in detail (cf. Alcock with Alcock 1988), the range of problems to be considered on a site-by-site basis would be broadly similar to those encountered during an equivalent evaluative exercise for Wales (Edwards and Lane 1988):

- the interpretation of very partial excavations, often not fully published;

- assessment of the likely timespans of sites whose last recognisable and datable artefacts – often items from the Roman world or on occasion post-Roman imports delivered along the Atlantic seaways – seemingly precede their demise by some time;

- evaluation of the significance of small quantities of imported pottery or datable metalwork with less than impeccable associations with the structural record on individual sites;

- consideration of what Alex Morrison (1974, 68) felt compelled, in a not-unrelated discussion examining evidence for medieval use of prehistoric settlement sites, to describe as 'intermittent continuity of occupation'.

[1] Calibration and re-assessment of radiocarbon dates obtained a generation ago is a specialist field led in this country by Mr Patrick Ashmore of Historic Scotland. In what follows, radiocarbon dates, where used, have been quoted in broad calendrical terms, based on data analysed by Ashmore and presented on Historic Scotland's web site.

His frustration, borne of the shallow stratification represented on some sites, combined with the partial nature of the evidence, applies too with regard to some first millennium AD sites.

A definitive catalogue of Pictish forts is thus likely to be some way off. None of this liturgy of woe, however, should be allowed to detract from the substantial headway made during recent decades in the delineation of hill-forts occupied during the Pictish period. Usable evidence from excavations has become available in previously-unimagined quantities; and, as others have insisted, stratified, well-contexted information is of key importance in the recognition of Pictish forts, since superficial form and locational characteristics have proved for some decades now to be such fallible guides (e.g. Close-Brooks 1986).

Scottish archaeology would certainly be the richer for a collaborative examination of our current knowledge of first millennium settlement akin to that edited for Wales by Nancy Edwards and Alan Lane (1988), from which the bullet-pointed remarks above are drawn. Despite the manifest incompleteness of the current overview, is it hoped nonetheless that the outcome – even if constructed very largely as one archaeologist's checklist of some of what has been established – will form a useful addition to the Groam House Museum papers.

The merits of hill-forts: architecture and society

Why focus primarily on hill-forts, when it will readily become apparent that the sites to which reference is made are far from presenting homogeneous characteristics? One reason is that their enclosing works – the walls, less frequently the ramparts and ditches – of many of these sites remain features of some visual significance in the landscapes of east and north-east Scotland. It is these barriers, in effect, which, in combination with locations that offer some topographic advantage, provide at least the appearance of strength and give rise to the defensive, even military, connotations implied by the epithet 'hill-fort'. Moreover, the enclosures which define these forts still comprise some of the most readily appreciable elite architecture in the area: the remainder – major timber buildings are an excellent example (Ralston 1997, 28-9) – is generally no longer apparent at ground level. Hill-forts are thus still archaeologically recognizable more widely than are other settlement types over much of Pictland.

As others – most notably Professor Alcock and his former students in the Glasgow School (Foster 1997, 10) – have cogently argued, these hill-forts moreover include key centres from which power was exercised in the Early Historic period (Foster 1998; Driscoll 1998; 2002). A dominant perspective in archaeological studies for some considerable time has been the reading of the settlement evidence as an intimation both of increasing centralisation and of the dissemination of authority over greater distances during the first millennium (e.g. Cottam and Small 1974; Watkins 1984; Alcock 1988; Driscoll 1992; Foster 1996). These hill-forts are thus in some instances and for some phases within the first millennium AD elite centres, places that contributed to the development of thanages and other territorial units within Pictland, as propounded for example by Driscoll (1991) for Strathearn.

As in first millennium AD contexts elsewhere (e.g. Dark 1994), there are indications that, for the inhabitants of Scotland, the size and apparent degree of architectural complexity of their settlements were intimately related to the organisation of social and political life. A number of Professor Alcock's contributions touch on this theme, whilst, for contemporary Ireland, aided by legal and other near-contemporary documentary accounts, Stout discusses this issue in detail in relation to the raths and cashels or ring-forts of that country (1997, ch 7). There, ring-fort size mattered, as did the scale of the enclosing works, both features – in theory at least – being directly related to status within a finely-graded elite. In a similar vein, in a consideration of Irish domestic buildings of this period, Murray (1979) has critically reviewed the contemporary documentary evidence for the status associations of buildings of particular sizes in relation to the products of archaeological excavation.

The architecture of a given site may thus have conveyed all kinds of direct visual signals about the importance of those who lived there to the Picts and their neighbours, although it may be doubted that strangers could ever infallibly read the status of the occupants from the scale and character of the buildings they encountered. Such idealisations as are found in the contemporary literature need to be tempered by an appreciation of what political and residential realities, modified by the availability of resources and of labour, may have entailed. 'Edifices, either standing or ruined', Dr Samuel Johnson contended in 1775, 'are the chief records of an illiterate nation' (1984, 85). Whilst their elites were certainly not illiterate, the Picts remain archaeologically protohistoric: thus the structural record represented by their settlement sites merits consideration as it provides a complement to views of the Picts for long, albeit quite reasonably, dominated by the iconographic and other evidence furnished by their sculpture on stone.

4

Intimations of the likely interplay between developing political complexity and the assumed concomitant emergence of settlement hierarchies need to be further nuanced in the case of the hill-forts of Pictland. Alcock (especially 1988) has demonstrated how these enclosed sites can convincingly be fitted into a pattern of intermittent residence by the uppermost tiers of the political elite during cycles of peripatetic movement. Such a system is a product of a state of affairs where it is easier for the leaders to move to the resources they require than for food renders and other products to be transported to the chiefs. To that extent the occupation of the forts can be accorded with a heterarchical state of affairs – in which the relative rank of individual sites can be established in a number of different ways (cf. Crumley 1985; Crumley and Marquardt 1987) depending on patterns of residence and wider geopolitical considerations – rather than a more straightforward, fixed hierarchical one. The perceived importance of settlement sites may thus have depended not solely on the 'hardware' of their location, fortifications, internal structures and stores, important as these would undoubtedly have been, but also on the 'software' of who was resident there and when. As in the big houses of Scottish estates in more recent times, the inhabitants of such settlements must on occasion have viewed with trepidation the arrival on their property of more distant elites with their retinues, not on account of any direct military threat that they might pose, but because of the demands that hospitality, such as the providing of feasts, would make on their food and other reserves. By way of comparison, McKean (2001, 61-4) discusses the potential severity of such impacts in the sixteenth and seventeenth centuries – at times access even to Stirling Castle had to be restricted because of the high costs imposed by such regimes of hospitality.

At a more prosaic level, as in other protohistoric contexts, the enclosures that surround hill-forts represent some of the major co-operative engineering tasks undertaken by groups within Pictish society that are straightforwardly recognisable in the archaeological record (cf. Ralston 1995). In the case of the Picts, however, it is important not to exaggerate the scale of these undertakings: none of the known works approaches the labour and resource requirements of, say, major linear earthworks constructed elsewhere in post-Roman Britain, such as Offa's Dyke near the Anglo-Welsh border, nor of major southern British Iron Age hill-forts, most famously Maiden Castle in Dorset, which are distinctly bigger sites. The great promontory fort at Burghead, on the southern Moray Firth coast, probably remains the most substantial single building project for which we have direct archaeological evidence (Small 1969, 1976), although not all the components of that much-damaged site are necessarily entirely post-

Roman constructions. Equally, whilst some of the architecture of Burghead's enclosures was undoubtedly elaborate, recent work at the position of the look-out station (which has produced the remains of a substantial stone-built dump as the fill of that bank: Melanie Johnson pers. comm.) suggests that not all of it was. Mapped to scale in relation to similar structures elsewhere across Britain, Burghead is clearly in the second rank in size terms (Alcock *et al.* 1995, illus. 11.1), although with an enclosed area considerably in excess of 2 ha it is the largest secular enclosed site that can definitely be attributed to the first millennium AD in Scotland after the abandonment of the successive Roman legionary bases. Were Pictish hill-forts meant to be military strong-points? The extent to which defensibility was a principal aspect of their importance is in large measure unknowable, although it would be very unreasonable completely to dismiss this function. In the Scottish perspective, it is noteworthy that students of the first millennium AD settlement record justifiably continue to lay stress both on the defensive aspect of hill-forts and on their roles as central places, including as key nodes overseeing pinch-points in the communications routes through the country. In such perspectives, comparisons may be made with how medieval fortifications worked, or by reference to manning levels for walls (approximately one soldier every 5m) quoted in Anglo-Saxon documents. The ethnographic record may also be examined for instances of the use of broadly-similar sites in warfare – as in the *pa* built by the Maoris of New Zealand. Contrastingly, for the first millennium BC during which physically-similar sites were constructed, this defence-led perspective has rather fallen from favour in contemporary archaeological thinking (e.g. Hingley, 1992; Armit 1997, 59). Whatever may be made of these enclosures as means of differentiating and organising space, as visible barriers separating those within from those beyond, and as signs and symbols of status and power, completely to eschew military considerations seems excessive and unnecessary. Sir Mortimer Wheeler (1952, 74), discussing other hill-forts, inevitably had the words: '... these fortifications are urgent things, dynamic reactions, possessing the anxious effort of men from age to age in a ... struggle to keep pace technically and tactically with the changing pace of attack. They have, often enough, little to do inherently with the less instant and more local vagaries of brooches and crockery ...'. Wheeler's emphasis on the potential separation of military and domestic culture would not now find general favour, but – given the manifest political instabilities and warlike tendencies of the period – coupled with the numerous instances in which their destruction by fire is attested, defence must be considered to have been a major purpose of these sites.

It is also of course the appearance of records of assaults on, and sieges of, such sites in the contemporary written sources that underscored Alcock's definition (1981) of some first millennium AD hill-forts as 'Early Historic' sites. His narrower usage of that term was deliberately restricted to those sites known from documentary sources that could also be identified archaeologically. Generally – although there are exceptions – such mentions of individual hill-forts make direct reference to warfare at them. None the less, enclosure is unlikely to have served only a single, defensive purpose. On the one hand, the construction, maintenance and appearance of such works certainly impacted on basic, everyday concerns for the society of the time (not least in terms of the consumption of resources); on the other their existence – in good repair or dilapidated condition – would have sent more abstract and symbolic messages to friend and foe alike.

Feachem's review

Richard Feachem's review, based on his 1952 paper, and thus now fifty years old, forms a convenient baseline against which to assess progress in our understanding of the enclosed sites of Pictland. Given its date, his approach was inevitably dominated by the twin considerations of defensive configurations – considered typologically – and topographic settings. Much had already been established by the time he wrote, albeit on grounds yet more slender than are today available. Feachem, for example, readily conceded that Pictish fortifications were likely to be heterogeneous in character, citing in support the substantial range of descriptors for such sites that Angus Graham's (1951, 65-8) consideration of Dark Age records had revealed. He also acknowledged the variety of purposes such enclosures might have fulfilled and by extension the potential variability of their forms over the period of several centuries during which they could have been built. It was moreover already plain that in first millennium AD Scotland '...structural fashions extended impartially across political divisions' (Feachem 1955, 71). The definition of an ethnically- or culturally-definable Pictish style of fortification was thus already acknowledged to be an illusion.

Ethnicity and architectural styles

It is important to emphasise this key point. In more recent decades, the apparent links between material culture and ethnic groups, for the first millennium AD and indeed more generally, have become the subject of renewed and more critical archaeological interest (e.g. Alcock 1987, fig 1;

Jones 1997), reinforcing the conclusion that the straightforward correlation of distinctive archaeological cultures in the sense envisaged by Gordon Childe with historically-named peoples is rarely wholly possible. We may thus surmise that the events that took place on the sites here labelled as Pictish, and the processes that lay behind them, were important in the flexible transformations in social and political life that gave rise to the Picts and the other named peoples of Early Historic Scotland. The accumulating evidence in the case of houses too (Ralston 1997) does not by any means suggest the former existence of an ethnically-consistent architecture across the Pictish domain. To that extent, the classical definition of archaeological cultures, as associated with Gordon Childe, is no longer apposite. In sum, it was in the places defined architecturally by the remains considered here, amongst others, that the Picts were forged as a people, rather than the contrary – a unified people creating a standardised architecture. To argue this, of course, is not to deny that for the people of those times the ethnic distinctions they perceived were other than real, vital and immediate, as historians continue to stress (Clancy and Crawford, 2001; Driscoll 2002).

Ring-forts

By the mid-1950s, Feachem was able to propose a range of architectural types that could be put forward as Pictish. The simple circular single-entrance enclosures then termed ring-forts offered him an obvious example of a relatively standardised set of monuments that included clusters of sites located well within the boundaries of Pictland as this was historically known. They still do, even if these structures are now interpreted very differently (as a variant on the substantial house tradition already established in the first millennium BC). As well as free-standing, independent examples, notably the series largely found within northern, Highland Perthshire (Taylor 1990 with earlier literature: Ill. 1), Feachem was able to put forward instances with potentially contemporary outworks (e.g. Tillycoultry, Clackmannanshire: Feachem 1955, fig. 2, a site now destroyed). Others, as he recognised, occurred in association with hill-forts – most famously within the suite of earthworks on Turin Hill in Angus (Alexander and Ralston 1999). Dunearn in Fife offered another case where such ring-forts sat substantially within, or partially overlay, the enclosures of earlier forts. The availability of these earlier works as convenient quarries for building stone, as well as the topographic advantage their positions conveyed, were put forward to account for the structural superimpositions apparent. To such arguments we might now add an

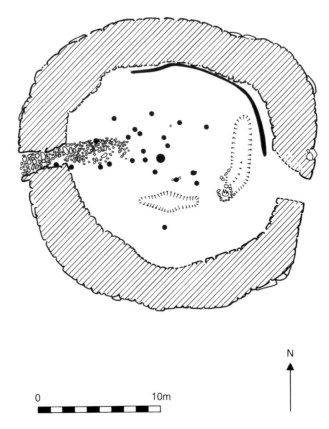

N

0   10m

*Ill.1 Allean, Perthshire and Kinross: The Queen's View homestead, showing
internal postholes and other features, suggesting a substantial house rather than
use as a 'ring-fort'. Redrawn by Eleanor Wilkinson based on Taylor 1990.*

awareness of the potential significance of the proximity of major earlier
monuments in emphasising by physical association the importance of the
inhabitants of their successors, as suggested by Driscoll (1998) in a wider-
ranging review, considered further below, of some of the royal centres of
early medieval Scotland.

Not all such dun sites were rigidly circular: Feachem added the small oval
or D-shaped duns (again with single entrances) that also occur in localised
groups within Pictish areas. Whilst numbers of such sites may well have
been in use during the first millennium AD, all should however, for the
meantime, be excluded from consideration as forts.

Timber-laced defences, including Burghead

Amongst architectural styles of fortification, it was already clear to Feachem that timber-laced walls, most notably that at Burghead – given its association with the celebrated Class I sculptured stones from the promontory – might belong to the Pictish period. It was also apparent by the time he wrote that most of the typologically distinctive series of oblong, vitrified, seemingly gateless forts – a series unique to this country – occurred within the Pictish heartland of eastern Scotland north of the Tay. The example on the Tap o' Noth, Aberdeenshire is considered subsequently: Ill. 19. These strands of evidence contributed to the prevailing view that advocated what is now considered an unacceptably-late, broadly early first millennium AD date for the occurrence of timber-lacing as a constructional trait of fortifications in Scotland. Childe (1940, 216) and Wheeler (1952), for example, were both prepared to consider the vitrified forts of Angus and Perthshire as the by-products of assaults by Agricola, leading to their destruction by fire. Others saw eastern Scottish hill-forts more generally in terms of a response to Roman activity (e.g. Simpson 1943). This was an intellectual world dominated by short chronologies, and by unwarranted assumptions of northern tardiness in the adoption of what were taken in more southerly areas to be conventional Iron Age cultural traits.

Feachem began to re-evaluate such perspectives. For instance, he was swayed by his opinion that the lowest wall-courses of the broch on the Laws of Monifieth, Angus, seemed to oversail the vitrified wall there as an indicator that at least that example was an earlier construction. Whilst that particular stratigraphic relationship has not been confirmed by subsequent observation, Feachem thus contributed to the lengthening of the chronology for such burnt examples of timber-earth-and-stone-built walls. This process has since proceeded apace, such that it would now be widely accepted that timber-laced walls in Scotland, burnt or not, were a feature of the first millennium BC as much as of the first millennium AD. In that regard it is interesting to note that some well-known examples, for long attributed to the pre-Roman Iron Age, have been put forward in more recent literature as potentially Pictish in date (e.g. Finavon, Angus, discussed below: Ritchie 1995a; and Castle Law, Abernethy: Close-Brooks, 1986). If nothing else, this emphasises the durability of the constructional style, and of its outcome once they had been set on fire.

Although views have been modified very considerably since the 1950s, timber-laced and vitrified walls remain a key component of our record of Pictish enclosed places; and wider questions of their dating are far from wholly resolved. In some instances, the application of different scientific techniques has given decidedly different outcomes for individual sites (see Alexander 2002 for a discussion relating to Finavon). Indeed, some analyses would suggest much earlier beginnings for the series of oblong vitrified forts, around 2000 BC in the case of Tap o' Noth, Aberdeenshire, (Sanderson *et al.* 1988), a date about which the present writer remains profoundly sceptical. Despite the continuing uncertainties in the date range to be attributed to such sites, it is manifestly the case that within Scotland timber-laced walls enclosing sites simply cannot be attributed to any particular narrow chronological span.

Citadel forts on craggy summits

Feachem (1955, 76) also pointed to craggy summits, often heavily fissured and dominated by extensive exposures of bare rock, as a preferred location for Pictish fortifications. He sub-divided these sites – which he called 'citadel forts' – into two series. Numerically the major set consisted of those then recently classified by Robert Stevenson (1949) as 'nuclear forts' (sometimes termed, less menacingly, 'nucleated forts'). On the periphery of Pictish territory, Dundurn, near St Fillans in Perthshire (Feachem 1955, fig. 9; Alcock *et al.* 1989) is the most fully examined example here (Ill. 2). The type-site for the other series of citadel forts was the enclosure on Dumyat, the westernmost summit in the Ochils of

Ill. 2 Dundurn, Perthshire and Kinross. This aerial view shows the nucleated fort, itself the product of successive remodellings of the defences around the craggy summit, and the cultivation terraces on the lower slopes.
Photo: Ian Ralston.

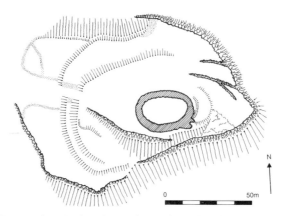

Ill. 3 Dumyat fort, Stirlingshire. Plan, redrawn by Eleanor Wilkinson, after RCAHMS 1963.

Stirlingshire (Feachem 1955, 76-8, with fig. 5). This latter group he characterised as consisting of a summit enclosure within, but not conjoined to, outer enclosures which are placed at lower altitudes (Ill. 3). These lower circuits generally adopt what may be described as conventional courses for hill-top works – that is to say they broadly follow the contours around the hill – with the distinction that they often run up to and stop against rocky outcrops or free faces. Dumyat is unexcavated, but the evidence of its place-name suggests a connection with the *Maeatae*, an Iron Age people recorded in Roman sources. More recent commentators – including the Royal Commission's investigators – have tended to see remains with these characteristics as indicative of multi-period works (e.g. RCAHMS 1963, no. 68; Stevenson 1985, no. 84), rather than envisaging that they were built, whatever their period, as a single concept.

Ill. 4 Mither Tap o' Bennachie, Aberdeenshire: the inner face of the dry-stone outer wall which partially encircles this remarkable granite outcrop. Photo: Ian Ralston.

Another possible example of this series noted by Feachem is the intriguing enclosure around the granitic tor of the Mither Tap o' Bennachie in Aberdeenshire (Shepherd 1996, no 74) (Ill. 4). Both it (at 518m) and Dumyat are notably high-altitude sites, widely visible over the lower valleys of important east-flowing rivers. Such hill-forts, despite the complexity of their enclosing works, call into question the likelihood, if not the feasibility, of permanent settlement within them, whatever the date of their construction. At least some of the buildings examined within the Mither Tap by that remarkable pioneering lady archaeologist, Christian Maclagan, in the 1870s (Maclagan 1875), must be secondary, because they were seemingly built over tumbled stonework, recalling the less clear evidence of secondary settlement within Craig Phadrig that is considered below. More than one phase of occupation is thus indicated. These sites are however at markedly higher altitudes than any of the hill-forts so far confirmed by archaeological excavation as being Pictish in date, although this does not rule out the possibility that they belong to the first millennium AD. Elsewhere in the country – as at Eildon Hill North in Roxburghshire – high altitude forts have been attributed to rather different periods of use (in that case, in the Late Bronze and Roman Iron Ages: Rideout *et al.* 1992), but the enclosed high-altitude sites of Scotland north of the Forth (including Tap o'Noth in Aberdeenshire, for which a variety of dates have been out forward: Gentles 1993 cf. Sanderson *et al.* 1988) and the undated Ben Griam Beg in Sutherland (Ralston and Smith 1983; Mercer 1991) remain poorly understood. In the case of the Mither Tap, we may note that its configuration of heavily-walled enclosure set below spectacular rock outcrop bears remarkable similarities to the Scotic site of Dunadd, discussed most recently by Campbell (forthcoming).

Ill. 5 Hill of Barra, near Oldmeldrum, Aberdeenshire. This small fort, surrounded successively by lines of rampart and by dry-stone walls, has several parallels in that county and suggests multi-period use.
Photo: Aberdeen Archaeological Surveys.

By the mid-1960s, when Feachem again reviewed the evidence (1966, 82-5), he had adopted the multi-period hypothesis for Dumyat and sites comparable with it that was elaborated in Royal Commission Inventories from the 1960s onwards. His view had now become that many of the oval-shaped innermost enclosures on a wide range of sites were indicative of the re-occupation, in late Roman or subsequent times, of pre-Roman Iron Age hill-forts, as in the stone-walled forts of central Aberdeenshire such as Hill of Barra near Oldmeldrum (Shepherd 1996, no. 76) (Ill. 5). In general, in the 1966 account, Feachem took a minimalist position on Dark Age hill-forts, conceding principally that the 'repair and strengthening' (Feachem 1966, 85) of earlier fortifications were likely during these centuries. In a sense, that 1966 contribution represents the 'high-water mark' of Scottish hill-forts as a substantially pre-Roman Iron Age phenomenon and for Feachem this position involved a significant move away from the view that he had previously taken. This change of perspective may have been coloured by the results of Feachem's work with the Scottish Commission – principally in the Border counties, where hill-forts seemed through the work of the Piggotts and others in the post-War period very substantially to be a feature of later prehistory. Since Feachem's mid-sixties re-assessment, on the one hand, some examples of hill-forts have been demonstrated to have early *floruits,* essentially within the later Bronze Age; and on the other, more particularly since Alcock published his influential chart in 1987 (Alcock 1987, fig. 4) it has become evident anew that several such sites – in Pictland, and indeed beyond – are indeed post-Roman constructions.

Long duns

Lastly, to return to the 1955 review, Feachem claimed a set of sites he termed 'long duns' as typical of the Pictish heartlands. The example he put forward as a type-site was Denork in Fife (Feachem 1955, 83 and fig. 10). This grouping was perhaps especially symptomatic of the desire to extract hypotheses on dating essentially from the physical form of such sites. The field evidence from individual examples suggests however that this proposition is problematic. The principal enclosure at Dunmore fort in Stirlingshire, at the northern end of the Campsie Fells, for instance, is of this form; and the characteristics of an outer wall at that site have been proposed as being comparable to Rubers Law in Roxburghshire, and hence possibly too representing a post-Roman construction (RCAHMS 1963, 76-77 and fig. 16). Overall, however, the evidence for the dating of long duns remains tenuous. They do not seem to have attracted excavation since Feachem considered them; and they are in any case not restricted to

Pictland, an example overlying what appears to be a conventional Iron Age hill-fort occurring at Peniel Haugh in Roxburghshire (RCAHMS 1956, 124-6 and fig. 163).

After Feachem: independent dating

If Feachem's 1955 survey was completed well before independent dating, by methods such as radiocarbon, became readily available, the next overview of the evidence, published by Lloyd Laing in 1975, was able to draw on the results of renewed, if still small-scale, programmes of excavation. In the Pictish heartlands, this included the work of Colvin Greig and the late Alan Small, who obtained the first radiocarbon determinations attributable to the Pictish period from fortifications. Laing was interested in demonstrating the continuing use of pre-Roman Iron Age settlement types into the centuries succeeding the Roman withdrawal and emphasised the evidence for hill-fort construction during the first millennium AD, which by then was beginning to accumulate. In some instances, even where excavations had not been carried out, he was able to reconsider the evidence from Pictland and to propose that certain classes of site, notably those termed by Feachem 'defensive enclosures' (as defined in 1966: Laing 1975, 8), might be attributable to the first millennium AD. Moncrieffe Hill, overlooking the lower Earn valley in Perthshire, was used as the type-site within Pictland for this class.

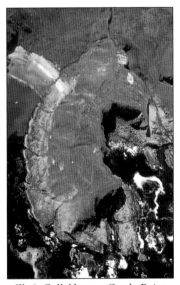

By 1975, Laing (1975, 12) was able to cite three forts (two of which are coastal promontories) with radiocarbon dates indicative of use during the Pictish period: Burghead (Small 1969), Cullykhan (otherwise known as Castle Point, Troup: Greig 1970; 1971; 1972) (Ill. 6), both promontories on the south coast of the Moray Firth, and – more problematically – Craig Phadrig on the outskirts of Inverness. What had until

Ill. 6 Cullykhan or Castle Point, Troup, Aberdeenshire: the multi-period promontory fort and adjacent Cullykhan Bay viewed from seaward. Excavations by Colvin Greig demonstrated that the site was in use at latest by the beginning of the pre-Roman Iron Age and continued into the first millennium AD. Photo: Aberdeen Archaeological Surveys.

15

that time been a substantially topo-graphical approach to site categorisation and chronology was thus beginning to be complemented by independent isotopic dating. Radiocarbon dates were thus one of the key products of these new excava-tions (Shepherd 1983), and were as important in the reassessment of post-Roman hill-forts as they had been a few years previously in extending the span of the pre-Roman Iron Age (cf. MacKie 1969).

The Alcocks and Early Historic fortifications

Since that time, the outstanding contribution to the development of Pictish hill-fort studies has undoubtedly been that of Professor Leslie Alcock, with his late wife Elizabeth and his students at Glasgow University (Alcock 1988). The suite of reconnaissance excavations undertaken on documented Early Historic sites within Scotland (Alcock 1981) includes several within Pictland. Of these, the evidence recovered from Dundurn, on the cusp with the Scotic territories of the West (Alcock *et al.* 1989), and Castle Urquhart, overlooking Loch Ness (Alcock *et al.* 1992), is, for present purposes, the most important.

The hill-forts as presently known

Dundurn

Pictish hill-forts clearly include *de novo* constructions – Dundurn appears to be a clear example – as well as cases of reoccupation, and sometimes re-commissioning, of enclosures of later prehistoric date (Ill. 2). Such practices are shared with other historically-attested groups within first millennium AD Scotland. Small-scale excavations at Dundurn, near St Fillans at the eastern exit from Loch Earn, provided Alcock (Alcock *et al.* 1989) with a convincing developmental sequence within the first millennium AD for this key nucleated fort. The reader is referred to that account as an example of a hugely-successful small-scale intervention by targeted excavation.

Clatchard Craig

Clatchard Craig, overlooking the lower Tay near Newburgh in Fife, was an important hill-fort, its position strengthened by sheer cliffs on its northern side. Now entirely removed by quarrying, it was one of the most extensively dug of known Pictish enclosed sites prior to its destruction. Planned by the Royal Commission in the 1920s (RCAHMS 1933, 4-6 and fig. 71), this hill-fort was partially excavated in the 1950s. The

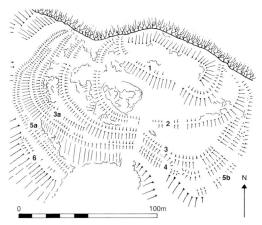

Ill. 7 Clatchard Craig, Fife: ramparts securely Early Historic in date are those numbered 1 to 3, but it seems highly probably that the whole system on this hill was of that period. Redrawn by Eleanor Wilkinson after Close-Brooks 1986.

unpublished evidence from this fieldwork was later expertly evaluated by Dr Joanna Close-Brooks (1986). This multivallate site is of particular importance amongst Pictish enclosed sites with regard to both the form and sequence of its enclosing works (Ill. 7). Radiocarbon dates for timbers contained within the ramparts, obtained as part of Close-Brooks' work, and a number of small finds, make it plain that its most important occupation fell entirely within the first millennium AD. Whilst the plan of the site suggests, on initial inspection, a pre-Roman Iron Age multivallate fort, with at least some of the banks running parallel with each other around parts of the hill, the principal ramparts examined – notably 1 and 3 – containing quantities of carbonised roundwood and locally displaying signs of vitrifaction, are radiocarbon-dated to the Pictish period. Dr Close-Brooks interpreted the evidence from rampart 3 as indicating that the original wall-face may well have been torn down to facilitate the burning of this wall. She also suggested that rampart 2, which she considered as the most recent defensive line examined in the 1950s work, not only included timber-lacing (identified through the recognition of gaps in its dry-stone wall-face), but also showed signs that the external wall face was originally turf-clad, a trait not yet recognised elsewhere in the Pictish repertory. Clatchard Craig is remarkable not least for the indications that it may have been enclosed by multiple timber-laced walls, but also because the indications of refurbishment consist in the addition of further walls, rather than (as might be anticipated in pre-Roman Iron Age contexts) the use of dump ramparts to envelop earlier walls when the need to re-commission these arose. Like a number of enclosed sites elsewhere in Scotland, Clatchard Craig also includes restricted evidence for the re-use of Roman masonry, probably from the Severan base at Carpow beside Abernethy: such deliberate imports from Roman works located at some distance from this hill-fort is a likely reflection of the prestige invested in its fortifications, and has parallels elsewhere. For the moment the defensive configuration of Clatchard – notably the presence of multiple timber-laced walls – still appears unique within Pictland.

A major feature of first millennium fortifications in Pictland apparent at Clatchard is the construction of vertically-faced walls using the three long-established components of stone, timber and earth or similar fill material. This admixture, used widely by the first millennium BC in a considerable variety of styles in temperate Europe, need not of itself surprise us. In the first millennium AD this combination still enjoyed general favour (e.g. Alcock *et al.* 1995), often being associated as is the case in Pictland with evidence of burning and vitrifaction. Elsewhere, in areas with limestone geologies, calcination arises from such practices.

Timber, earth and stone in first millennium AD fortifications

The Pictish heartlands share the use of such timber-and-stone fortifications with many areas of contemporary Europe. Instances known to the writer extend from Scandinavia, for example in the main wall of the substantial 112 ha hill-fort at Torsburgen, Gotland (Engström 1984), to tenth century Viking fortresses in Denmark. Very different in character are complex linear frontier works such as the Danevirke in southern Jutland, the repair of which, also using timber, is securely dated by dendrochronology to 737 AD (Jansen 1992, fig 10.4). The consumption of timber in walls has also been recorded into northern central Europe as for example in the eighth to eleventh century works at Naszacowice in Poland (Poleski 1992). The significant wooden components within the walls of well-preserved sites like Behren Lübchen in the former East Germany provide indications of the considerable resource implications of such structures in terms of timber consumption (illustrated by Herrmann 1989, 604). Similar works also occur much further west in the late first millennium AD: the wall of the heavily vitrified promontory fort of the Camp de Péran, Plédran, in Cotes d'Armor, Brittany, has been attributed to the early tenth century AD (Nicolardot 1997). Within Britain itself, the key comparison for the Pictish sites is with Rampart E at South Cadbury, Somerset (Alcock *et al.* 1995 illus. 2.6).

In this regard, the evidence from Pictland thus conforms to a widespread, but variable, European tradition. New instances of first millennium AD hill-forts displaying indications of structural timberwork within their defences, sometimes in the form of vitrified stonework, continue to be identified in Pictland. Recently, SUAT's work at the Abbey Craig provided a further instance of vitrified stonework from the slope below the Wallace Monument near Stirling (Bruce Glendinning, pers comm. & 2001). Professor Alcock's research programme on Early Historic sites confirmed another example within Pictland at Castle Urquhart beside Loch Ness (Alcock and Alcock 1992). The use of timber in wall constructions (resulting on their destruction, in some instances, in vitrification) is however, not established in all areas of Scotland. Confirmed examples of first millennium AD timber-framed ramparts remain absent from some areas even close at hand, for example in Dalriadic western Scotland (Lane and Campbell 2000, 239).

There is, furthermore, evidence for considerable architectural diversity in the styles of these fortifications within Pictish areas. Both one phase at Dundurn (Perthshire) and part of the circuit at Burghead (Moray) have provided evidence for iron spikes (true nails at Dundurn, but apparently headless examples at Burghead), almost certainly initially augured into intersections between elements of the timber framework. At the latter site the evidence for the occurrence of nails within the defences is intermittent and the most recent excavator of the main wall, Alan Small (1969) seems not to have recovered any iron spikes, despite finding traces of former timberwork, in the form both of the voids for longitudinal planks set in the wall-face and of burnt material from the wall core at the seaward end of the site (Ill. 8). Experiment shows that theoretically such burnt, indeed vitrified ramparts might also conserve the remains of iron nails (Ralston 1986a) but no instances of this are recorded in Pictland. A rather earlier, pre-Roman Iron Age case of this is attested in Normandy and there is an enigmatic nineteenth-century account (MacLagan 1875, 101), referring to a site at Templaw, Dundonald in Ayrshire, which may be an example, but this is the sole reference to iron in vitrified material from Scotland known to the present writer. Other examples may of course await discovery.

As has been argued elsewhere, such elaborate timber-laced walls were not only conspicuously resource-consuming constructions, but equally – where it occurred – their destruction by fire would also have been a considerable spectacle (Ralston 1986a), more especially at night. The inclusion of iron nails in such walls – famously otherwise known in the *muri gallici* of the Gauls who faced Julius Caesar – is, as was the case on the earlier continental sites, an indication that iron is unlikely to have been in short supply. This is important, for acidic soil conditions have

Ill. 8 Burghead, Moray: voids indicating the former positions of the timberwork in the inner wall-face of sandstone slabs as revealed in Alan Small's excavations of 1966. No nails were encountered during this campaign, although they were found elsewhere in the fortifications in some of the XIXth century excavations at the site. Photo: James Livingston.

contributed to a general difficulty in assessing the importance of that material in first millennium AD Scotland.

Multivallation at Burghead and elsewhere

In some views, the presence of multiple lines of fortification, although attributable at Clatchard Craig to the first millennium AD, is a feature more characteristic of later prehistoric forts than those of the subsequent period. In fact, across western and northern Britain, there is plentiful evidence to challenge this view (e.g. Dark 1994). In the case of Burghead, all the excavation work to date has been on the innermost enclosures –

those enveloping the upper and lower courts (Edwards and Ralston 1978, with earlier bibliography).[2] As regards the now substantially removed series of ramparts and ditches at the landward end of the site, it remains possible to argue that they were either essentially part of the same Pictish project to enclose the site, a view favoured by the present writer, or that they were earlier, and thus probably a later prehistoric, system. Comments on their variable size and varying alignments in MacDonald's description (1861, 344-5) might even be read to suggest that they themselves did not form a unitary work. Few of the other bi- or multi-vallate Moray Firth promontories, such as Cleaved Head, near Macduff, have been excavated, and the key site at Dundarg failed to produce good dating evidence (Wainwright 1954; Fojut and Love 1983), so they cannot be pressed into service as a guide to the date of the landward ramparts and their accompanying ditches at Burghead. It may, at some future date, prove possible to examine these features at Burghead – the former ditches are still marked by undulations in the streets of the modern village – or the surviving fragment of the innermost rampart, which forms the Doorie Hill, now crowned by The Clavie, the epicentre of Burghead's January fire festival, in order to resolve this issue.

Multivallation should certainly not be excluded as potentially a feature of Pictish fortifications, the inland promontory site at Inchtuthil, Perthshire – close to the important Flavian legionary fortress – providing another possible example (Ill. 9). This promontory fort displays five ramparts and ditches and further internal defensive features, aligned obliquely to them, the latter recovered by excavation in 1901. Both excavation and plan evidence (Abercromby et al. 1902; RCAHMS 1994a, 52-4), however, suggest multi-period construction. The innermost and most massive of the ramparts (trenched in 1901) included dressed blocks of stone re-used from the neighbouring Roman fortress, a characteristic of some Pictish forts already noted above. An area of paving (Abercromby et al. 1902, fig. 20), initially interpreted as a hearth, but more recently proposed by RCAHMS as part of a building, was examined within the arc of the innermost (apparently palisaded) enclosure line. This floor also included recycled Roman masonry. Whilst the evidence for at least re-use of this small site during the post-Roman period is compelling, it is far from clear that the multiple lines of rampart drawn straight across the promontory must all date to this period. It may also be remarked in parentheses here that the

[2] These comments were written before the writer's 2003 excavation at Burghead funded by the Burghead Headland Trust. Whilst these confirmed the survival within the present-day settlement of elements of the landward banks and ditches shown on Roy's plan of Burghead, no new dating evidence for them was recovered.

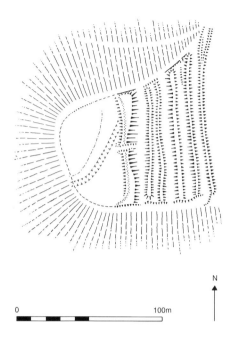

N

0   100m

*Ill. 9 Multivallate defences at the Inchtuthil promontory fort, near Meikleour,
Perthshire and Kinross. Redrawn by Eleanor Wilkinson after RCAHMS 1994a.*

palisade line noted at the site may equally date to post-Roman times,
adding another fortification technique – also known elsewhere – to the
potential Pictish repertory. Multivallation, it may be remarked, certainly
occurs elsewhere in the British Isles in promontory sites of the first
millennium AD (e.g. Dark 1994). A famous case from Ireland (also
involving the reconfiguration of an earlier site) is at Dunbeg, in County
Kerry (Barry 1981; Edwards 1990).

Scatness and the reoccupation of earlier sites

In terms of indications of reoccupation, the nature of the evidence for the
use of individual forts can be exiguous and therefore enigmatic. A
relatively recently-excavated example that highlights this problem is
provided at the south end of Shetland by the diminutive promontory
blockhouse fort of Scatness, near the West Voe of Sumburgh, sheltering
behind a single bank and internal ditch. Activity in its Phase 3 amounted
archaeologically to a small quantity of human food debris and the

positions of a series of small fires set in the lee of the blockhouse. These were fixed by a series of calibrated radiocarbon dates to around AD 600 – 900. Stephen Carter and his co-authors interpreted these traces as an intimation that the ruins of the earlier periods of use of the site retained an importance in the Pictish period: '… these ancient buildings had perpetuated something of the society that had built them for … centuries after the cause of their construction had slipped from memory …' (Carter *et al.* 1995, 480). This is as good an explanation as any for the ephemeral 'reoccupation' attested by the evidence rehearsed above.

Craig Phadrig

The well-known site of Craig Phadrig, set above the Beauly Firth to the west of Inverness, offers a rather different and to some extent perplexing case of reoccupation, worth rehearsing in some detail. Here, two lines of enclosure are known on an oblong vitrified fort that has been repeatedly examined since the eighteenth century (Small and Cottam 1972). The absence of charcoal from the unconsolidated fills of its inner, stone-revetted wall means that its dating is dependent on radiocarbon dates from contexts much less securely related to wall construction. Samples were recovered respectively sealed under the wall itself or within its tumble (Small and Cottam 1972, 23); these point – although far from incontrovertibly – to a date around the middle of the first millennium BC for the building of this structure. The outer rampart is much less regularly preserved and is seemingly much more variable in its initial construction. The presence of a thin layer of heat-affected stone, considered to have been collected from the inner rampart to be used as a capping over the outer work (Small and Cottam 1972, 29-30 and fig. 7, 36), allows the suggestion that this rampart has at least two main periods of construction represented within it. A single radiocarbon date for charcoal, again – with reservations – attributable to around the middle of the first millennium BC, may thus only fix the first constructional episode; one for peat recovered elsewhere in association with this wall must be considered much less useful as an indication of constructional date, as it furnishes the broadest of *terminus post quem* associations (Small and Cottam 1972, 34). From the evidence rehearsed by the excavators, it may be tentatively concluded that the isotopic determinations bracket the initial constructions of the fortifications within the pre-Roman Iron Age, but that the posited refurbishment of the outer wall could theoretically be of any date thereafter. It would not be unreasonable, in light of the artefactual evidence for first millennium AD occupation, to conclude that this undated refurbishment of the outer wall was Pictish.

The most recent excavators of Craig Phadrig also obtained localised evidence from within the inner enclosure (Small and Cottam 1972, fig. 8) for the presence there of a considerable depth of stratified deposits. The two main occupation horizons identified both seemingly overlay tumble from the inner wall, intimating their potential lateness in the sequence of use of the site; furthermore, they were generally separated by an archaeologically-sterile layer containing charcoal attributable, on calibration, to a broad span either side of the birth of Christ (2030 BP ±100 uncalibrated: N-1118). The upper occupation horizon, again apparently associated with tumbled debris from earlier constructions which made the definition of buildings unachievable, none the less included some structural evidence (both a clay floor and, at a number of separate locations, hearths) as well as animal bone, whet-stones and coarse stone items, two sherds of the robust pottery called E ware imported from Gaul (Thomas 1981) and the mould fragment for a hanging-bowl escutcheon. Both Ewan Campbell and Alan Lane (1994, 111) have suggested that the mechanism by which the former material – considered to have been used in Britain as storage containers rather than as cooking vessels – arrived in the Inverness area was through secondary gift-giving from the Scotic West; such pottery may date to the first half of the seventh century. David Longley (1975) attributed the mould to the manufacture of an escutcheon of his Type 1a, thus a fitment for a bowl of broadly fifth-to-sixth century AD date; the late Robert Stevenson (1972) proposed a date around AD 600 for this piece. It is strongly indicative of on-site manufacture of high-status metalwork. This horizon within Craig Phadrig also produced a single radiocarbon date (1540 ±85 BP uncalibrated: N-1119) which, after calibration, suggests a date of around the third to seventh centuries AD for its context.

Craig Phadrig merits discussion, despite the problems of fixing the chronology of its ramparts, because some of the artefactual evidence from it, notably the imported pottery and the escutcheon mould, implies an elite component, and on-site manufacturing, associated with the later re-occupation of this hill-fort. Against this, the evidence for refortification at this time is most safely described as not proven; and the implication of the accumulation of superimposed deposits in the heart of the site seems clearly to point to settlement within – and over the debris of – a substantially ruinous enclosure of earlier date. Nor does the evidence as I read it point to a brief episode of squatting comparable to that suggested by apparently casual later first millennium finds – including a fine ninth-century penannular brooch – from manifestly earlier enclosed sites like Aldclune near Blair Atholl in Perthshire (Hingley *et al.* 1997). Understanding the late re-occupation of Craig Phadrig thus needs markedly contrasting evidence to be reconciled, but Cullykhan (discussed below) also provides evidence for repeated use during the first millennium AD. At Cullykhan too, some of the first millennium AD evidence overlay considerable accumulations of tumbled wall material. Other examples of the oblong vitrified forts also have associations with later first millennium material. The Doune of Relugas in Moray, for example, is the findspot of a number of ringed pins (Fanning 1983).

More contentious evidence for re-use

Evidence for the repeated use of promontory forts will be discussed below, but in other cases the indications of first millennium AD re-use of hill-forts within Pictland is rather more contentious. The famous site at Finavon in Angus, dominating Strathmore, and near the well-known sculptured stones at Aberlemno, may serve as an example. Although much of the evidence from this impressive enclosed site excavated by Childe in the mid-1930s points to its construction and use during the pre-Roman Iron Age, notably the small finds as Dr Euan MacKie has recently emphasised to the writer, a suite of thermoluminescence dates for the substantial vitrified wall pointing to seventh-century AD activity has rekindled interest in a possible Pictish context for the site (Ritchie 1995a). Meantime, these determinations stand as an isolated testimony of possible first millennium AD use of the site, and should perhaps be treated with reserve. Derek Alexander offers a new plan and discussion of Finavon (2002), but simply presents the divergent chronological information it has furnished. Close-Brooks (1986, 148) has also put forward the possibility that – as at Clatchard Craig – the enclosures around other hill-top sites may be of more recent vintage than the pre-Roman Iron Age material traditionally used to date them – Castle Law at Abernethy is a case in point, and this is a hypothesis that deserves continuing consideration.

Two Moray Firth promontories: Cullykhan and Green Castle, Portknockie

Leaving aside Burghead, two of the other coastal promontory forts on the southern shore of the Moray Firth show evidence of first millennium AD occupation and enclosure following use of the same locations in the first millennium BC. Both are, interestingly, close to sheltered bays suitable for beaching boats, and thus may have been places where Pictish sea-craft may have been stationed. As on other stretches of coast, it seems that there are two series of promontory forts on the Moray Firth coast: those with ready access to the sea (Burghead, and the site of Dunnottar Castle, overlooking the North Sea, to the south of Stonehaven, both considered below, also fall into this category) and those set along longer stretches of cliffed coastline, where going down to the sea in ships would have been much harder to achieve: Dundarg is an example of this second series. It is noteworthy that confirmed Pictish examples are all instances where the possibility of a direct maritime role for the site can be hypothesised on the basis of an adjacent shelving beach, although the Alcocks' work at Dunnottar on the castle site itself did not produce certain first millennium AD evidence (Alcock and Alcock 1992).

Colvin Greig's examination of Castle Point, Troup (also known as Cullykhan) near Gardenstown, in the 1960s and early 1970s, was proportionately the most substantial intervention on any later prehistoric and early medieval enclosed site in Scotland at that time. Unsurprisingly, in retrospect, it provided evidence for a bewildering array of uses of the promontory, culminating in recent centuries in the service of part of the flat-topped promontory as a bowling green, and the construction at its seaward end of a Napoleonic era fort. The known history of enclosure on Cullykhan begins with the construction of a palisade at its landward end, subsequently replaced within the Early Iron Age by an elaborate timber-and-stone wall flanking an entrance passage. Seaward of this a timber-laced wall was subsequently constructed, not simply barring access to the promontory but also set above the eroding cliff to the north. This fortification – its full areal extent does not seem to have been defined – was built with a foundation raft of transversal timbers; its destruction by fire provoked vitrification. A final early phase of fortification is indicated by two ditches drawn across this sector of the promontory. Radiocarbon dates roughly bracket much of the use of this central part of the site in the earlier first millennium AD, but there are no sure indications that it was still fortified by the middle of that millennium (Greig 1970; 1971; 1972).

Equally set obliquely to the general trend of the coastline, in this instance east of the modern harbour at Portknockie (Ill 10), the Green Castle (Ralston 1980; 1987a) protects the sheltered coastal waters of the Triple Creeks, where until relatively recently boat-building was carried out, from the open sea. The promontory also enjoys distant views across the inner firth as far as the cliffs of eastern Caithness, a strategic position perhaps of particular importance for this small site when the opposing coastlands were in the Scandinavian domain. Already in use and occupied during the later Bronze Age, two elements of the Green Castle in Pictish times need detain us.

*Ill. 10 Portknockie, Aberdeenshire: the Port Hill, with the Green Castle to the
right of it, shelter the modern harbour. Photo: Ian Ralston.*

One of these is the fortification that survives – albeit capped and damaged
by fish-drying platforms of nineteenth-century date – on its landward side.
Did this feature also previously run along the top of the cliff on the
seaward side, as comparison with Greig's work at Cullykhan (1970, 1971,
1972) would allow, and as is securely demonstrable for Burghead? Any
such wall at this position must have been removed by erosion during the
intervening centuries: certainly it was not identified here in excavation.
We therefore do not know whether this wall originally defined a wholly
enclosed area, like the upper and lower courts at Burghead, although it can
also be argued that the architectural elaboration of this wall strengthens the
comparison with Burghead. With the cliff on the seaward side crowned by
a substantial wall, these coastal sites would have looked imposing to
arrivals by boat as well as those travelling over land. Strong off-shore
winds along this coast may also have provided an environmental
justification for the continuation of the circuit in some form along the
seaward edge of the site. There, it would undoubtedly have reduced the
chances of the inhabitants being blown over the cliff in the gusty
conditions that frequently prevail.

Despite the damage to it in more recent times, the wall of this promontory
fort is of particular interest. Built at the same position as an earlier palisade
and slighter fence lines, it had been destroyed by fire, the burning only
provoking the vitrificaction of the stonework in a very localised manner.
Contrastingly, the lowest courses of the heavily-carbonised timbers within

Ill. 11 Portknockie, Aberdeenshire, the Green Castle: carbonised timbers within the Early Historic timber-laced wall. The inner wall-face survives on the right; the outer, originally set downslope to the left, has been lost. Photo: Ian Ralston.

the wall survived very well (Ill. 11). The wall was built of prepared timbers, with some evidence for the incorporation of planks and of roundwood. At least some of the timber was re-used, since individual beams contained numerous mortice-holes, including ones which were non-functional at the time the wall was destroyed. The inner wall-face sat on the level surface within the fort, and there was unambiguous evidence that it was built over the lowest course of horizontal timberwork. Although the excavated evidence is limited to a single beam, it points unambiguously to the timberwork showing in the wall-face akin to the manner that Alan Small (1969; 1976) noted at Burghead. It also suggests that during construction the timberwork was assembled first, with the stone wall-face being added secondarily as a cladding (a constructional sequence also proposed by Nicolardot {1997} for the contemporary Camp de Péran, near St Brieuc in Brittany). Since only the basal courses of the inner wall face survived at the excavated position, it is not possible to say whether, in effect, the entire timber framework was first erected, or whether the whole construction proceeded in successive, more-or-less horizontal, stages. The identification of a vertical element set into a half-check in one of the transversal horizontal beams gives a pointer to the three-dimensional characteristics of the timber framework, which was clearly not simply a series of horizontal rafts as is proposed most usually for Scottish timber-lacing. Interestingly, Alan Small (1975, 82) posited the former presence of vertical timbers as a component of the timber-lacing of Craig Phadrig.

Contrastingly, the preservation of the outer part of this wall was radically poorer, for it must originally have been built downslope on the southern, landward side of the promontory. Although some features survived here, subsequent erosion, both natural and man-made, meant that they could not be unambiguously related to the surviving wall structure. The building of the outer wall face downslope – an economical method of providing a wall with external height whilst economising on labour and materials – is a device recorded on other important elaborately-walled forts of this period. The Alcocks' examination of *Alt Clut*, the British stronghold at the confluence of the Leven and the Clyde at Dumbarton, provides an excellent example (Alcock and Alcock 1990, fig. 11). We did not observe anything that would provide a parallel for Dr Close-Brooks' hypothesis, developed at Clatchard, of the preliminary partial demolition of the wall before it was set on fire at the Green Castle. The nature of the timber framework within this wall is best paralleled at the other end of Britain, on another site examined by Professor Alcock: Cadbury-Camelot in Somerset (Alcock *et al.* 1995), although the south-western example is some two centuries older in date. Despite its diminutive size, the Green Castle, Portknockie, thus seems to be a fully-fledged member of the set of forts enclosed by elaborate, resource-consumptive walls. Given the evidence for the re-use of timbers, the radiocarbon dates for this wall need not be as intimately connected to its use as one would like, but it would not be unreasonable to conclude from them that this was a fort that was operational when Norse longships were plying the waters around the Firthlands of the eastern Highlands.

The other principal feature of the Pictish Green Castle is the survival within it of a rectangular building with a dry-stone-faced wall, some 4m wide and with rounded corners. Sadly, only one end of the building survives, but its minimum length is 7m (Ill. 12). A single internal postpad – from the position of which it would be possible to argue for two internal rows of roof supports and thus a three-aisled building – was present. Whilst this proposition is far from incontrovertible, it is clear that this building did not derive its structural strength from earthfast posts, and it is easy to imagine beams of the sort found re-employed in the fortification having originally been employed in such a construction. At the outset, however, the writer took the view – in light of the surviving timberwork of ships such as those famously sunk at Skuldelev to block Roskildefjord in Denmark – that the fortification wood might have come from dismantled

Ill. 12 Portknockie, Aberdeenshire, the Green Castle: remains of dry-stone walled internal structure, suggested as a minor feasting hall. Photo: Ian Ralston.

ships from the Pictish 'navy': in retrospect, this seems excessively fanciful. Anna Ritchie (1995b) has speculated that this building may have been the feasting hall of a minor chief, and that is certainly possible. The Portknockie structure is clearly different from the great timber-built feasting halls, such as the Doon Hill examples in East Lothian (Reynolds, 1980; Alcock *et al*. 1995, 132-9 and illus. 11.3), or putatively Pictish examples further north, like that at Monboddo (Ralston 1984, 74; Foster 1996, fig. 35). There are, however, examples closer in scale elsewhere, as at Cruggleton in Galloway (Ewart 1985), and some of the lesser timber buildings at Yeavering (Northumberland) (Alcock 1993, 34-5).

The likelihood of varieties of partially stone-built rectangular architecture in later Pictland – never remote because of the elite associations of masonry with the Church for which we have eighth-century testimony – has been strengthened by the discovery and examination of the architecturally very different Pitcarmick series of buildings in the uplands south of the Mounth (RCAHMS 1990; Stevenson 1991; Ralston 1997). In the case of the Portknockie building, however, there are no elite materials amongst the associated artefacts to bolster Ritchie's interpretation. Equally there is nothing to suggest that this building may have been a chapel, which is a possibility that perhaps needs to be considered, in light of the former presence of St Aethan's chapel (the associated graveyard still survives) built on the line of the one of the landward ramparts at Burghead.

Other aspects of Moray Firth promontories: Burghead and Dundarg

General Roy's famous late eighteenth-century plan (Small 1969) of that promontory makes it plain that a walled graveyard apparently occupied part of the medial line of the former triple ramparts, indicating that these had fallen out of use as serious defensive features during early Christian times, a reversal of the sequence advocated by MacDonald (1861), for whom the graveyard preceded the banks and ditches. It may be significant that other instances – themselves rare – of ecclesiastical sites at the locations of earlier hill-forts in the British Isles suggest that this is an Irish phenomenon (Dark 1994, 41). Stones from this chapel at Burghead were removed in the nineteenth century, but surviving sculptures, including parts of a corner-post shrine, point to the importance of the site as a centre of early Christianity, perhaps around AD 700 (Thomas 1971; Shepherd 1993). This is the only known chapel site located physically within a Pictish hill-fort, and is a further pointer to the exceptional character of the Burghead evidence.

Re-examination (Fojut and Love 1983) of the other promontory fort for which a precocious Christian association has been claimed – Dundarg to the west of Rosehearty (Ill. 13) – has cast doubt on the earlier

Ill. 13 Dundarg, Aberdeenshire: aerial photograph of the promontory fort investigated by Fojut and Love seen from seaward. Note the lack of a neighbouring bay cf Cullykhan and other coastal promontory sites discussed passim. Photo: Aberdeen Archaeological Surveys.

interpretation and on the structural evidence put forward both for an early fortification and a chapel site associated with St Drostan amongst the excavated buildings there (Simpson 1954; Wainwright 1954). Simpson's case for a building towards the apex of the promontory being an early chapel (1954, 48-52, with fig. 5) has been dismissed by Fojut and Love (1983, 450), who consider the series of buildings of which this is one as seventeenth- rather than seventh-century in date. The answer to Simpson's rhetorical question (1954, 52) is that as yet there seems to be no archaeological evidence to square with the marginal note in *The Book of Deer*, which might allow this site to be '... the original establishment planted by St. Drostan within the ramparts of the mormaer Bédé the Pict's *cathair* at Abbordobor'. Contrastingly, although there are certainly early finds from the site (Fojut and Love 1983), neither of the apparently early sets of defences – the outer components of the system investigated by Wainwright; and the new alignment identified in the more recent excavation – is securely dated. Whilst the possibility of a Pictish constructional phase cannot be excluded, it is noteworthy that the 'Red Fort' suggested by Dundarg's place-name (Simpson 1954, pl. 1) does not enjoy the same ready, but sheltered, sea access provided by an adjacent bay that can be seen at Cullykhan, Portknockie and Burghead.

Reverting to consideration of the evidence from Burghead, the 'Bailey's Well', the remarkable rock-cut cistern approached by a set of steps set within the lower court of the fort, is more problematic to interpret. Considerably altered since its early nineteenth-century discovery, it has been assumed, prosaically, to have been an elaborate well, guaranteeing the water supply of the promontory's Pictish inhabitants. The contemporary documentary sources make frequent mention of sieges, increasing the importance of ready access to drinking water. Alternative explications, from locale for ritual drownings, through water shrine, to early Christian baptistery have been proposed (Shepherd 1996, no. 72). Ian Shepherd has suggested more recently that it may have been formed a particular challenge in an initiation ritual (pers. comm.). The absence of corroborating evidence makes it extremely difficult to select from amongst these options, and there must be the possibility that, during centuries when belief systems were clearly undergoing profound changes, the pool of fresh water may have been used successively for several of these purposes. To that extent, the Bailey's Well may be taken as another possible intimation of early Christian activity within the fort. Whilst unique in its architectural detail, artificial cisterns or pools are known within a range of other forts, including Moncrieffe Hill and the Green Castle, Portknockie.

Entrances

Given the major interest in Pictish fortifications, it is disappointing how little can still be said about the entrances to them, and more generally of the buildings and other features that they contained.

In the case of hill-forts securely attributable to the first millennium AD in Pictland, no entranceway has been the subject of excavation, in several instances as a matter of deliberate policy (Alcock *et al.* 1995, 131). In other cases, the positions of the gates seem to have been unclear, as for example at Clatchard Craig, where the programme of works on the ramparts focussed exclusively on straightforward rampart cuttings. At Portknockie, the causeway across which access to the Green Castle was obtained had been quarried away as part of the late nineteenth-century harbour works. Given this state of affairs, there is simply little solid evidence available to be rehearsed.

The illustration purporting to show an entrance to the inner fort at Burghead in Professor Martin Carver's splendid recent survey (1999, 30-31) provides an artist's impression that graphically exemplifies the separation between what may be envisaged from a theoretical perspective and the general lack of directly-pertinent archaeological data. An imposing, wide entrance with a dry-stone walkway, fronted by a stone parapet carried over it on longitudinal beams, has been envisaged. This seems an appropriately monumental architectural context for the approaching military elite who are also illustrated in the reconstruction, reminding us that, particularly in relation to a peripatetic aristocracy, such liminal locations as the entrances into major settlements must have been important arenas for display, confrontation, and the like. The wall in the vicinity is depicted with the Class I sculptures set in its outer face: but as will be argued below this is difficult to sustain. The gate itself, not in view in the reconstruction drawing, must be assumed to be recessed towards the inner margin of the entrance passage. None of this, sadly, is directly underpinned by archaeological evidence, and to the present writer the suggested architecture seems over-elaborate. Of course, the fort at Burghead did have entrances, as Roy's plan, prepared before the wide-scale damage to the site in the nineteenth century, makes clear. A single, approximately aligned, passage runs through the trivallate outer works; it may also have been possible to approach the site along the shore beyond the eastern end of these works. Both the upper and lower courts were also noted by Roy's draughtsmen to have entranceways placed approximately medially in their landward ends; and a further gap is shown above the cliff at the seaward end of the upper enclosure. After nearly one hundred and fifty years of excavation, albeit very intermittent, at the site, none of its entrances has been examined, and most no longer survive.

The only solid evidence concerning the gateways to Pictish forts is still that contained in Adomnan's description of Columba's arrival at the *munitio* of King Bridei, in which we learn that the gate could be locked. Sadly, we are provided with no information as to whether this gate opened inwards – as would be anticipated in medieval structures – or outwards, as is often suggested in the case of Iron Age hill-fort entrances, where these are constructed on a slope. From the available archaeological evidence, however, there are no indications that the entrances to Pictish hill-forts were protected by additional lines of earthwork or similar devices, such as are encountered in some pre-Roman Iron Age hill-forts.

Domestic occupation and the forms of buildings within forts

In contrast to the substantial successes of recent years in recovering domestic architecture from a range of settlements around peripheral Pictland, and the recognition of numbers of unenclosed near-rectangular structures in the uplands of Perthshire (Stevenson 1991), our evidence for domestic and other buildings within Pictish hill-forts remains very weak (Ritchie 1995b; Ralston 1997). To date, architecture of the 'ventral', cellular and 'figure-of-eight' forms recovered from the North and West of Scotland seems not to have been recovered within enclosed settlements: in the far North, even the multi-cellular 'Shamrock' at Gurness in Orkney, lies outwith the ditch that envelops the broch there (Fojut 1993), although in Lewis broadly similar buildings constitute several of the later recognisable building phases (Phases 9-4) within the shells of the earlier broch at Beirgh on Lewis (Harding and Gilmour, 2000, figs 4a & 4b). There is no suggestion, however, that by the time these buildings were erected, the old broch wall had any defensive significance whatever, and indeed there are indications that it was reduced in height during the cellular building phases identified by the excavators.

For the hill- and promontory-forts, the available evidence for buildings within them is far from plentiful. Such as it is, however, that evidence does seem to point towards a preference for rectilinear structures, as has already been noted in the case of the Green Castle at Portknockie. In light of broadly contemporary evidence from elsewhere in Britain, the difficulty of discerning building plans should not occasion too much surprise. In general, by the middle of the first millennium AD, buildings were becoming structurally much less reliant on earth-fast (and thus archaeologically recoverable) elements. Post-pads and sill-beams are amongst the constructional elements that can be anticipated in Pictland; Loveluck (1998, 152-4 and fig. 6) reviews the co-existence of a range of building styles on a Lincolnshire Anglo-Saxon site, and the technical devices that gave rise to them might also have all been available during the later first millennium AD in Pictland. Attention has already been drawn to the re-used beams with mortice and other joints within the wall at the Green Castle in this context. Any building with such a rigid structural framework would not have required earthfast posts set in post-holes.

The earliest relatively comprehensible report of excavated evidence for internal buildings comes from the late nineteenth-century work at Burghead. Accounts of earlier observations of structural details during the reduction and quarrying of that site (e.g. MacDonald 1861), leaving aside the cistern or baptistry, discussed above, are largely incomprehensible. An enigmatic comment by Young (1893, 90) on an excavation he conducted within the lower enclosure at that site may, however, be indicative of the former presence, not only of individual buildings, but also of a planned layout there. What may have been rectangular structures, described as having walls three feet thick and in one instance thirty feet long, were noted. When encountered, these walls had already been damaged by ploughing. These structures are described in the late Victorian account as being 'placed in a row on each side of the fort'. Loosely associated with these buildings (lying between them and the rampart, but not apparently stratigraphically related) was a midden containing animal bone which overlay an iron axe and other items. Such an arrangement is currently without parallel in the Pictish repertory, and it may well be advisable to discount it in the present context as it potentially forms the remains of a later settlement established within the earlier fort. There are, however, rare if comparable examples elsewhere of arrangements of rectilinear buildings which seem to belong in a mid-to-late-first millennium AD context; buildings on the small tidal island of Gateholm, Pembrokeshire (Edwards and Lane 1988, 73-5 and fig. 14), for example, would seem to fall into this category.

Other buildings identified to date include those within Urquhart Castle, again identified during reconnaissance excavations carried out by Glasgow University (Alcock and Alcock 1992). As at the Green Castle, Portknockie, the postulated structures at Urquhart are rectangular, although the surviving evidence for them, encountered in a relatively narrow trench, in this instance included post-holes and areas of cobbling. It is also proposed that these buildings may have been keyed into the inner

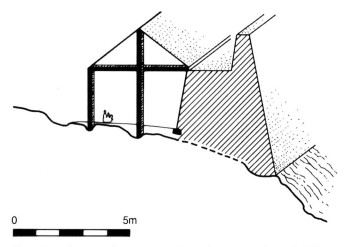

0   5m

Ill. 14 Urquhart Castle, Inverness-shire: diagram, redrawn by Eleanor Wilkinson, showing hypothesis for rectangular structures constructed against the inner wall-face of the fort as put forward by Alcock and Alcock 1992.

wall-faces of the enclosure wall (Alcock and Alcock 1992, fig. 26) (Ill. 14). Small's (1969; 1976) examination of the timberwork associated with the inner wall-face of the upper court at Burghead led to a similar suggestion being made for that location, although no supporting evidence seems to have been gleaned from the extension of the excavation into the interior of the fort there.

Contrastingly, inferences about the form of buildings derived from the shape of hearths are generally insecure. Such features are often far from indicative of the shape of the building in which they were set, one exception occurring in cases where the position and shape of a hearth would seem to have in part dictated the groundplan of the associated building. This has been argued in Trench F at Clatchard Craig, for example, where a rectilinear hearth was recovered hard against the back of a rampart, an arrangement precluding a circular structure there (Close-Brooks 1986, 144-5). Finally, it is salutary that, despite the evidence that hill- and promontory-forts are a feature of the area that in due course formed the heartland of Pictland from early in the millennium through to about the eighth century AD, there are no unambiguous instances of excavated and securely dated first millennium AD round-houses from any example known to the writer, although circular buildings occur within forts of this date elsewhere in Britain (e.g. Alcock 1993; Dark 1994).

The storage of surpluses

Given the apparent importance of post-Roman hill-forts as centres for consumption, it is noteworthy that, with one debatable exception, none of the Pictish examples known to the author has furnished any direct structural evidence for the storage of agricultural surpluses. The exception is again Burghead where in 1809 a deep wood-lined pit apparently filled with carbonised barley was encountered near the point of the promontory (MacDonald 1861, 359). Nothing more is known of this undated feature. It has, of course to be acknowledged that not all storage technologies need be readily recognisable in the archaeological record. Of those documented from later prehistoric times, however, such as souterrains, bell-shaped storage pits, or substantial four-post structures, none has been recorded within and contemporary with a first millennium AD hill-fort in Pictland. In this regard, however, hill-forts are unexceptionable – archaeologically recognisable storage facilities seem rarely to be recorded on British settlement sites of the first millennium AD. This may be because they were components of the 'normal' buildings of this period: for example the semi-subterranean elements of houses like those at Easter Kinnear, Fife, may have been used in this way. Nor to date are there any unequivocal signs of specialised buildings for livestock within forts, although in the Pitcarmick series of upland buildings in Perthshire, and in the record of stone buildings from Pool, Sanday, Orkney, such structures have been recognised in the archaeological record of first millennium AD farms in Pictland.

Pictish forts and Pictish stones

Although further discoveries of Pictish Class I stones continue to be made, including a piece from the important Orcadian settlement at Pool on Sanday (Hunter 1997, pl. 4), none has been recovered from within a hill-fort since just after the First World War (Mack 2002, Appendix F). It was then that the only unambiguous rival to the Burghead bulls was found, the slab depicting a bullock recovered within the fort on East Lomond Hill, Fife (Corrie 1926). Burghead, where it is considered that the "famous bull carvings once adorned the wall of the upper fort as symbols of strength and ferocity" (Ritchie 1995b, 23), remains in this regard, as in so many others, exceptional. A mid-Victorian account (MacDonald 1861) states that some thirty such stones were originally encountered in the early nineteenth-century constructional works on the site; those that survive today were for the most part relocated when the harbour and adjacent buildings were modified in mid-century (MacDonald 1861; Romilly Allen and Anderson 1903). The direct association between fortification walls and Pictish stones, encapsulated in the sentence just quoted, present in the newer of the guidebooks (e.g. Ritchie and Ritchie 1998, 135) and illustrated by Carver (1999), is however unproven and is not, to the present writer's knowledge, to be found in print before 1993.[3]

Ill. 15 Dinnacaer rock stack and the Aberdeenshire coast looking south from Strathlethan Bay, to the south of Stonehaven. Dinnacaer is centre foreground, with the promontory of the Bowduns to the left; behind, on the far side of Castle Haven, lies Dunnottar Castle. Photo: Ian Ralston

The only other potential association of this type known to the writer is with finds made early in the nineteenth century at the conglomerate tidal rock-stack of Dinnacaer on Strathlethan Bay to the south of Stonehaven (Ill. 15). Dinnacaer, already precipitous by Victorian times, seems to have been subject to further erosion since its description by Romilly Allen and Anderson (1903), and its narrow summit, covered by a matted grass sward which would disguise any surviving remains of archaeological interest, is now only accessible using climbing gear. One of the six symbol stones from this location was found, apparently built into a wall, at the top, but the remainder (part of what seems originally to

[3] Where on the site of Burghead were the sculptured bulls found? Professor Stuart of Aberdeen seems to have seen several of them during a visit in 1809 when he speaks (at a time when Burghead was advocated as a Roman station) of '... baked bricks and tiles, half burnt beams of wood, broken cornices and mouldings of well-cut freestone, along with the figures of various animals ....' (quoted in Young 1890, 155), a listing not entirely believable. When MacDonald compiled his account (1861, 355-6, with pl. XI), three were known of the 'about thirty small figures of bulls' found at the time of Stuart's visit coincident with the early nineteenth century construction of the harbour. In a footnote (no. 2, 355-6), MacDonald drew attention to the rediscovery of a fourth such slab during the laying of a railway along the south quay while his own researches were under way. This example, as described to MacDonald by an un-named friend, was water-worn, and might have been collected from the shore. MacDonald explicitly remarks that "None of these bulls appear to have formed part of any larger piece of sculpture, *or to have been ever built into a wall*" (1861, 356: my emphasis). By the time of Romilly Allen and Anderson's account (1903 {1993} 118-24), six Class I bulls were known: whilst find-spots are discussed where these are known with any precision (see also RCAHMS, 1994b, 12), in no case is an association with the fortification – then already well-known through the work of MacDonald (1861) and Young (1891, 1893) - advanced. The '...famous series of bull stones apparently mounted high on the wall as a frieze...' was put forward by Ian Shepherd (1993, 79), in what seems to have been an unfortunate mis-reading of MacDonald's comments discussed above in an otherwise-perceptive account of Burghead and related sites in Moray. Similarly the slab displayed in the British Museum bears the label: 'They were probably brightly painted and set in the walls of the fort, making an impressive sight.' Splendid as is the vision of a fortification so decorated, there is no known archaeological evidence to support it, although it should be conceded that the possibility that the stones were recovered during the early nineteenth-century quarrying of the ramparts for constructional materials cannot be ruled out.

have been a larger collection) were recovered from the rocky shore below, having apparently been thrown down from the summit in the early part of the nineteenth century (Ralston and Inglis 1984, no. 20, with earlier bibliography). The collection has been re-evaluated by Alcock and Alcock (1992, 276-81), who have pointed out that these stones all seem to be 'plaques rather than stele' (1992, 280), a trait shared with the slabs from Burghead (although Ian Shepherd cautions that at least some of these may have been trimmed after their discovery) and East Lomond. This rather unusual characteristic of these stones may indicate that they were displayed in a particular way at these locations; but any direct connection with fortifications seems to be 'not proven'. In any case, several of the Dinnacaer stones are sufficiently atypical that their inclusion within the Pictish canon has been questioned (Mack 2002).

Juxtaposing the known distribution of Class I Pictish stones with the cropmark record, however, allows the possibility that other examples were associated with enclosures now invisible at ground level, but potentially originally of hill-fort type. A good instance of this possibility is offered on the former lands of the farm of Mains of Rhynie, above the Water of Bogie, near Rhynie in inland Aberdeenshire. Some eight stones from here, including the 'Rhynie man' now in Aberdeenshire Council's headquarters (Shepherd and Shepherd 1978, with previous bibliography), mostly come from the general vicinity of a multiple enclosure occupying a low eminence above the river course (Shepherd 1983, pl. 1; Ralston 1987b, pl. 19). It may be noted, however, that these examples seem to be conventional stele, rather than the plaques that characterise the Class I assemblages from Dinnacaer and Burghead.

Contrastingly, none of the forts within Pictland as this is historically known have produced any evidence for the existence of carvings in Class I style on exposures of living rock. Whilst such surfaces were clearly deemed appropriate for this kind of embellishment within the Pictish heartland, they are within caves, most celebratedly at Covesea in Moray (Shepherd 1993, with previous bibliography) and in the group at East Wemyss in Fife (RCAHMS 1994b). It is only outwith Pictland that the symbols occur on rock faces within hill-forts, one of several patterns in the recovery of these remarkable features that is potentially replete with ideological significance. There are two main examples of rock faces so carved within forts. The boar within Dunadd in Argyll forms part of a wider suite of carvings that has been reviewed by Lane and Campbell (2000, 18-23) and considered further in the context of the inauguration of the Dalriadic kings by Campbell (forthcoming). Although long accepted as an outlier of the Pictish symbol-carving tradition, Campbell puts forward cogent reasons to dismiss the Dunadd hog from the repertory of Pictish symbols and to consider it rather in the context of the deliberate melding of cultural traditions that characterised eighth-century Dál Riata. The other examples occur on the west side of the entrance passage of the fort on Trusty's Hill at Anwoth, in the Stewartry of Kirkcudbright (RCAHMS 1994b, 6, with earlier bibliography), far removed geographically from the remainder of the series. These are less easy to dismiss as Pictish work, in that they form a pair, one of which is an example of a widely-distributed symbol. The occurrence of overt, unusual symbols of all kinds at the peripheries of distributions has been noted in other archaeological contexts in relation to the need for particular populations – perhaps in the minority or otherwise threatened – to have special identifiers (Wells 2001, 70). It would hardly be novel to suggest that this might account for these carvings, and thus perhaps also for the absence of similar features on outcrops within the hill-forts of Pictland itself. As another instance of such a pattern, it may be noted that the occurrence of Pictish symbol stones in association with brochs seems to be a feature essentially of Orkney (RCAHMS 1994b, 19-20), although perhaps also affecting the opposite shore of the Pentland Firth at Crosskirk (Fairhurst 1984, 100-1). A new discovery from Old Scatness, Shetland (Anon 2002) extends this northerly focus.

Locational characteristics and the scale of sites: some observations

The significance of coastal locations as places for more-or-less informal markets has been a favoured theme of first millennium AD research around the North Sea and the Baltic in recent years (e.g. Ulriksen 1994). In Denmark, the prototypes of such sites appear around the third century AD, and probably a few centuries earlier in the form of temporary settlements (Jansen 1992). Their development correlates with the intensification of craft enterprises, the expansion of trade, and presumed or demonstrated technical developments in Migration Period ships. In southern Scandinavia, available evidence shows that these sites can be quite variable in scale; they are frequently enclosed. In many areas, such sites may be set some distance from the coast itself, intimating that use was made of navigable rivers to gain access to more inland areas. In the Pictish heartland, however, navigable rivers offering opportunities for direct inland penetration over any distance are few. It may therefore be suggested that in this area coastal sites with marine access were dual-purpose, on the one hand acting as centres for craft-production and/or exchange; and, on the other, particularly from the 790s onward, serving as bases for the Pictish fleet facing the developing hostile strength of the Norse.

Favoured locations for pulling ashore boats would be sheltered, gently-shelving beaches such as that at the Triple Creeks at Portknockie. Manoeuvring boats onto land is easier on beaches covered with rounded pebbles and cobbles, rather than sand, as is the case, at least at present, there. The surviving exotic item from Burghead, the silver mount in Anglo-Saxon Trewhiddle style from a blast horn, could be accommodated in the use of that remarkable site in these ways, with the most likely areas to beach the boats lying on the west side of the promontory (Ill. 16), now very substantially altered by the building of the modern harbour and associated facilities, or at the former bay on the east side, shown on Roy's plan. Alternatively, as Webster (1991, no 247) has suggested, the occurrence of this remarkable piece so far north may result from 'Viking intervention'.

Ill. 16 Burghead, Moray: the surviving extremity of the promontory fort viewed from seaward. Photo: Aberdeen Archaeological Surveys.

Other possible members of this series would include the unexcavated promontory fort of the Maiden Castle, near Arbroath, which has a particularly impressive univallate enclosure (Ill. 17) and a neighbouring pebble-covered beach, the massive bank being different in scale from that of other coastal promontories in Angus, which are generally rather earlier in date (Ralston 1986b). It may not be coincidental that Maiden Castle is the nearest of the Angus defended promontories to the important early Christian site at St Vigeans.

Ill. 17 The substantial bank and ditch at the Maiden Castle promontory fort, near Arbroath, Angus, being inspected by a party of students. Photo: Ian Ralston.

Elsewhere on the coastal edge of the Pictish heartland north of the Tay estuary, the most extensive proposed member of this series is that at The Bowduns, the headland between Downie Point, which closes the bay at Stonehaven on its southern side, and that now occupied by Dunnottar Castle (Alcock and Alcock 1992, illus. 29) (Ills 15 & 18). The Alcocks put it forward as an alternative location for Dun Foither, following the – for once – disappointing results of their single-trench intervention at Dunnottar Castle itself, which failed to identify any early medieval activity there. Their account of the surface evidence (1992, 281-2) at The Bowduns is balanced and sanguine. Close to the rock stack at Dinnacaer, the nineteenth-century Ordnance surveyors of Bowduns reckoned there was a ditch and rampart drawn across its neck. The latter feature in particular may be described as doubtful, and clarification will require the spade. But if the Alcocks are right in relocating *Dun Foither* here (albeit the case for abandoning the traditional site at Dunnottar is not compelling), the Bowduns at some 6ha would become one of the most extensive enclosed sites north of the Mounth, and larger than any currently attributable to early medieval times.

Ill. 18 Dunnottar Castle, Aberdeenshire (see also Ill. 15). Aerial view of the site, also including the small promontory fort on the cliff edge identified during the Alcocks' campaigns. Photo: Aberdeen Archaeological Surveys

At the start of this account, the point was made that the more extensive hill-forts have, in some hypotheses, been correlated with periods of increased centralisation or hierarchisation in early societies (e.g. Ralston 1987a and b). In that view, drawing on the slender historical documentation from the first centuries AD, the pattern within the Pictish heartland suggests the increasing coalescence of social groups - tribes – during this period. An initial push factor encouraging the emergence of larger political units in the northern half of Scotland may have been the presence of Roman military units – the vanguard of the Empire - on their southern fringes. Assuredly too, such a process of coalescence is unlikely not to have stalled or been reversed, at least intermittently, or to have been more effective in some areas rather than others. It is thus improbable that the settlement record can be read to suggest a simple progression from simpler to more complex societies through time.

Using the building of the major hill-forts of the Pictish heartland – leaving Burghead aside – as proxy evidence, is there any new evidence to be adduced in support of the idea that the biggest hill-forts – such as the Group 1 forts in the North-East (Ralston *et al.* 1983) – were in use in Pictish times? In fact, the outcome of most projects over recent years

Ill. 19 Tap o' Noth, Rhynie, Aberdeenshire. The gateless oblong fort surrounding the summit overlaps a putatively earlier fort visible in this view. The outermost line lies downslope, towards the upper margin of the heather.
Photo: Aberdeen Archaeological Surveys.

seems to point to such sites belonging in essence to the pre-Roman Iron Age in this region, although the evidence is still scarce. In the case of the Brown and White Caterthuns of Angus, examined as part of the Edinburgh University Archaeology Department Field School in the 1990s, none of the fortification lines that was sectioned is a post-Roman construction (Andrew Dunwell pers. comm.). Furthermore, the most substantial site in the North-East, that enclosed by the relatively insubstantial outer bank on the slopes of Tap o' Noth, outwith the celebrated oblong vitrified fort, now looks less likely to have been in use in Pictish times than once seemed to be a possibility, in light of stray finds from its vicinity and the presence relatively nearby of the Rhynie Class I sculptures (Ill. 19). It has been noted (Ralston *et al.* 1983) that the spill from this tumbled wall overlies platforms within, and putatively related to, the outer wall line, so that the latter enclosure should on these slender grounds be the older of the two circuits on this remarkable hill. Archaeomagnetic dating (Gentles 1993) brackets the firing of the inner wall between the second century BC and early in the first century AD. The outer enclosure is therefore putatively older, and thus a potential example of a big, early fort, such as has been confirmed through recent work at Traprain Law and is also intimated at Eildon Hill North (Rideout *et al.* 1992) - both sites once prime candidates for Scottish minor *oppida* (Feacham 1966). In so far, then, as increasing hill-fort size may have in some times and places a correlation with deepening social complexity and more extensive political units, the Pictish heartland meantime seems not to comply with the hypothesis.

In contrast to Craig Phadrig and Cullykhan, for example, there are reasons to suggest that there was no late re-occupation within the vitrified enclosure at Tap o' Noth. The clearest evidence is provided by the surface indications for an earlier enclosure partially sealed by the vitrified fort, recognised by Andy Dunwell and Richard Strachan, suggesting that subsequent internal occupation was never sufficiently intense to eliminate this early feature. The White Caterthun in Angus offers a very different case, for here surface traces of two circular features, one potentially palisaded, within the great boat-shaped walled enclosure are most readily accommodated as features more recent in date than the lightly-vitrified wall itself, and thus more akin to the stone-built features within Turin Hill in the same county (Alexander and Ralston 1999).

Amongst other major hill-forts, a number in the North-East are unfinished. The Hill of New Leslie should probably be added to those listed as being in that condition by the writer and others (Ralston *et al*. 1983, 169, Table 3), which included Durn Hill and Little Conval. In Angus too, there are big, unfinished sites, as marked by the outermost line at the Brown Caterthun and by the incomplete works on Kinpurney Hill south of Meigle, with its noteworthy collection of Early Medieval sculpture. The most remarkable feature at this, the biggest site in Angus, is a detached inturned entrance, which takes advantage of the natural configuration of the hill, and points unerringly towards Schiehallion. Consideration of such orientations has found favour recently in studies of pre-Roman Iron Age forts, but cannot be claimed as of demonstrable chronological significance.

In considering such sites at the wider, British scale, Feachem (1971, 20) remarked that a variety of reasons for their abandonment, some related to external aggression, some related to local factors, could be advanced to account for their incomplete condition. Traditionally, the use of the forts in the North-East was linked to the Roman advance (Simpson 1943, 60-6), in a view that was, however, without direct archaeological support. Of the unfinished forts, none has been excavated, so that there is presently no justification for assuming that the construction and abandonment of some, or all, of them, might lie in the post-Roman period. Such a view cannot of course be excluded either, but meantime there seems no reason to link the most extensive hill-forts within the Pictish heartland with events and processes during post-Roman times in the first millennium AD.

Elite locations in relation to cemeteries of square barrows and earlier monuments

Stephen Driscoll (1998) has recently developed the idea that kings and other powerful early medieval inhabitants of Scotland made use of locations hallowed by the survival there of earlier monuments to reinforce their status. In eastern Scotland, the classic location where such a juxtaposition can be seen, at least in aerial imagery, is Forteviot in the Earn Valley (Alcock and Alcock 1992; Driscoll 1998, fig 3). The terrace at Forteviot displays an important complex of Neolithic monuments, rectangular barrows of first millennium AD date, and intimations of a late first millennium centre (not as yet including a feasting hall); an important early church is also indicated by the find of a sculptured arch. On analogy with the situation elsewhere in Britain, the physically close association between secular and religious elites may be anticipated (e.g. Dark 1994, 15). Forteviot lacks an enclosed site of the kind discussed here, but it may be asked whether examples of any of the other elements noted at the site might point to other possible cases. Does high-status burial or ecclesiastical evidence ever intimate nearby high-status enclosed settlement in Pictland? One instance may be hinted at by the cemetery of square barrows and other features at Red Castle near the mouth of the Lunan Water in Angus (Alexander 1999), located close to the promontory on which sits the later stone-built castle that bears the same name. Given the wealth of the surrounding cropmark record, it is possible that occupation of the Red Castle headland may have started in the first millennium AD, but excavation would be required to test this possibility.

Conclusions

In this account, the writer has tried to pick out some of the trends in the evidence for Pictish hill-forts that have emerged over the time since Feachem's overview. As Feachem had already recognised, the hill-forts of Pictland, both those securely established and others for which the evidence is little more than surmise, display very considerable diversity in their form and, in so far as it has been yet examined, their internal arrangements. It seems safe to predict that the variability of such enclosed sites will continue to increase as more sites are investigated – perhaps especially in the lowland zones of likely destruction amongst the potentially-relevant cropmarks – in years to come. In the meantime, the high-status associations of Pictish hill-forts seem clear for some sites, but by no means them all: Dundurn and Craig Phadrig may stand here as examples of sites with artefacts betokening wealthy associations and on-site manufacturing. Internal buildings that could be considered locales for elite action remain rare in the archaeological record; Ritchie's interpretation of the incomplete structure within the Green Castle at Portknockie as the feasting hall of a minor chieftain (Ritchie 1995b, 23) may be correct, but the building concerned is decidedly narrower than (say) the timber hall within the palisaded enclosure at Monboddo in former Kincardineshire (Ralston 1984).

Pictish hill-forts are still, as they were in Feachem's account, in the main a phenomenon of the area south and east of Inverness. Whilst much new evidence has accumulated, solid information about some aspects of these sites – such as entrances and internal buildings – is pitifully limited. There remains much to investigate.

References:

Abercromby, J., Ross, T. and Anderson, J. 1902 "An account of the excavation of the Roman station at Inchtuthil, Perthshire, undertaken by the Society of Antiquaries of Scotland in 1901", *Proc Soc Antiq Scot* **36** (1901-02), 182 - 242.

Alcock, L. 1981 "Early historic fortifications in Scotland", in *ed.* Guilbert, G. *Hill-fort Studies. Essays for A. H. A. Hogg*, 150 - 180. Leicester: Leicester University Press.

Alcock, L. 1984 "A survey of Pictish settlement archaeology", in Friell and Watson, 7 - 41.

Alcock, L. 1987 "Pictish studies: present and future", in Small, 80 - 92.

Alcock, L. 1993 *The neighbours of the Picts: Angles, Britons and Scots at war and at home*. Rosemarkie: Groam House Museum Trust.

Alcock, L., with Alcock, E. A. 1988 "The activities of potentates in Celtic Britain AD 500 - 800: a positivist approach", with Appendix "Enclosed places 500 - 800 AD" {by E. A. A.}, in *eds* Driscoll, S. T. and Nieke, M. R., *Power and politics in early medieval Britain and Ireland*, 22 - 46. Edinburgh: Edinburgh University Press.

Alcock, L. and Alcock, E. A. 1990 "Reconnaissance excavations on Early Historic fortifications and other royal sites in Scotland, 4: Excavations at Alt Clut, Castle Rock, Dumbarton", *Proc Soc Antiq Scot* **120**, 95 - 149.

Alcock, L. and Alcock, E. A. 1992 "Reconnaissance excavations on Early Historic fortifications and other royal sites in Scotland, 5: A: excavation and other fieldwork at Forteviot, Perthshire, 1981; B: excavations at Urquhart Castle, Inverness-shire, 1983; C: excavations at Dunnottar, Kincardineshire 1984", *Proc Soc Antiq Scot* **122**, 215 - 287.

Alcock, L., Alcock, E. A. and Driscoll, S. T. 1989 "Reconnaissance excavations on Early Historic fortifications and other royal sites in Scotland, 3: Dundurn", *Proc Soc Antiq Scot* **119**, 189 - 226.

Alcock, L., with Stevenson, S. J. and Musson, C. R. 1995 *Cadbury Castle, Somerset. The early medieval archaeology*. Cardiff: University of Wales Press.

Alexander, D. L. 1999 "Redcastle Barrow Cemetery", *Current Archaeol* **166**, 395 – 397.

Alexander, D. L. 2002 "The oblong fort at Finavon, Angus: an example of the over-reliance on the appliance of science?" in eds Ballin Smith, B. and Banks, I., *In the shadow of the brochs. The Iron Age in Scotland*, 44 - 54. Stroud, Gloucestershire: Tempus.

Alexander, D. L. and Ralston, I. B. M. 1999 "Survey work on Turin Hill, Angus", *Tayside and Fife Archaeological Journal* **5**, 36 - 49.

Anon 2002 "Old Scatness and the broch lairds of the Northern Isles", *Current Archaeol* **177**, 382 – 390.

Armit, I. 1997 *Celtic Scotland*. London: Batsford / Historic Scotland.

Barry, T. B. 1981 "Archaeological excavations at Dunbeg promontory fort, Co Kerry", *Proc Roy Ir Acad* **81C**, 295 – 330.

Campbell, E. (forthcoming) 'Royal inauguration in Dál Riata and the Stone of Destiny'

Carter, S. P., McCullagh, R. P. J. and MacSween, A. 1995 "The Iron Age in Shetland: excavations at five sites threatened by coastal erosion", *Proc Soc Antiq Scot* **125**, 429 - 482.

Carver, M. 1999 *Surviving in symbols. A visit to the Pictish nation*. Edinburgh: Canongate Books / Historic Scotland.

Carver, M. 2001 "Tarbat Discovery Programme (Tarbat parish) Early medieval settlement", *Discovery & Excavation in Scotland* NS **2**, 64 - 65.

Chapman, J. C. and Mytum, H. C. eds 1983 *Settlement in North Britain 1000 BC – AD 1000. Papers presented to George Jobey, Newcastle upon Tyne, December 1982*. Oxford: Brit Arch Rep Brit Ser, **118**.

Childe, V. G. 1940 *Prehistoric communities of the British Isles*. London & Edinburgh: Chambers.

Clancy, T. O. and Crawford, B. E. 2001 "The formation of the Scottish Kingdom", in eds Houston, R. A. and Knox, W. W. J. *The New Penguin History of Scotland from the earliest times to the present day*, 28 - 95. London: Allen Lane in association with the National Museums of Scotland.

Close-Brooks, J. 1986 "Excavations at Clatchard Craig, Fife", *Proc Soc Antiq Scot* **116**, 117 - 184.

Corrie, J. M. 1926 "Notice of ... (2) a symbol stone from East Lomond Hill, Fife , recently presented to the National Museum," *Proc Soc Antiq Scot* **60** (1925-26), 27 – 34.

Cottam, M. B. and Small, A. 1974 "The distribution of settlement in southern Pictland", *Medieval Archaeol* **18**, 43 - 65.

Crumley, C. L. 1985 "Pattern recognition in social science", *Social Science News Letter*, Fall 1985, 176 - 179.

Crumley, C. L. and Marquardt, W. H. 1987 "Regional dynamics in Burgundy", in eds Crumley, C. L. and Marquardt, W. H. *Regional dynamics. Burgundian landscapes in historic perspective,* 609 - 623. London: Academic Press.

Dark, K. R. 1994 *Discovery by design. The identification of secular elite settlements in western Britain, AD 400 – 700*. Oxford: Tempus Reparatum = Brit Archaeol Rep Brit Ser **237**.

Driscoll, S. T. 1991 "The archaeology of state formation in Scotland", in Hanson and Slater, 81 –111.

Driscoll, S. T. 1992 "Discourse on the frontiers of history: material culture and social reproduction in early Scotland", *Historical Archaeology* **26**, 12 - 24.

Driscoll, S. T. 1998 "Picts and prehistory: cultural resource management in early medieval Scotland", *World Archaeol* **30**, 142 - 158.

Driscoll, S. T. 2002 *Alba: the Gaelic kingdom of Scotland, AD 800 – 1124*. Edinburgh: Birlinn / Historic Scotland.

Edwards, K. J. and Ralston, I. B. M. 1978 "New dating and environmental evidence from Burghead fort, Moray", *Proc Soc Antiq Scot* **109**, 1977 - 78 (1980), 202 - 210.

Edwards, N. 1990 *The archaeology of Early Medieval Ireland*. London: Batsford.

Edwards, N. and Lane, A. eds 1988 *Early medieval settlements in Wales AD 400- 1100. A critical reassessment and gazetteer of the archaeological evidence for secular settlements in Wales*. Bangor and Cardiff: University of Wales for the Early Medieval Wales Archaeology Research Group.

Engström, J. 1984 *Torsburgen. Tolkning av en gotländsk fornborg*. Uppsala: Archaeological Studies Uppsala University Institute of North European Archaeology.

Ewart, G. E. 1985 *Cruggleton Castle: report on excavations 1978-81*. Dumfries: Dumfries and Galloway Natural History and Antiquarian Society.

Fairhurst, H. 1984 *Excavations at Crosskirk Broch, Caithness*. Edinburgh: Soc Antiq Scot Monogr Ser, **3**.

Fanning, T. 1983 "Some aspects of the bronze ringed pin in Scotland", in *eds* O'Connor, A. and Clarke, D. V., *From the Stone Age to the 'Forty-Five*, 324 – 342. Edinburgh: John Donald.

Feachem, R. W. 1955 "Fortifications", in Wainwright, 66 – 86.

Feachem, R. W. 1966 "The hill-forts of northern Britain", in *ed.* Rivet, A. L. F., *The Iron Age in northern Britain*, 59 - 87. Edinburgh: Edinburgh University Press.

Feachem, R. W. 1971 "Unfinished Hill-forts", in *eds* Hill, D. and Jesson, M. *The Iron Age and its hill-forts*, 19 – 39. Southampton: Univ Southampton Monogr Ser, **1**.

Fojut, N. 1993 *The brochs of Gurness and Midhowe*. Edinburgh: Historic Scotland.

Fojut, N. and Love, P. 1983 "The defences of Dundarg Castle, Aberdeenshire", *Proc Soc Antiq Scot* **113**, 449 – 456.

Foster, S. M. 1996 *Picts, Gaels and Scots*. London: Batsford / Historic Scotland.

Foster, S. M. 1997 "The Picts: quite the darkest of the peoples of Dark Age Britain?", in Henry, 5 - 17.

Foster, S. M. 1998 "Before Alba: Pictish and Dál Riata power centres from the fifth to late ninth centuries AD", in Foster *et al*, 1 - 31.

Foster, S. M., Macinnes, A. and MacInnes, R. eds 1998 *Scottish power centres from the Early Middle Ages to the Twentieth Century*. Glasgow: Cruithne Press. = Univ Glasgow Postgrad School Scott Stud, **2**.

Friell, J. G. P. and Watson, W. G. eds 1984 *Pictish studies. Settlement, burial and art in Dark Age northern Britain*. Oxford: Brit Archaeol Rep Brit Ser **125**.

Gentles, D. 1993 "Vitrified forts", *Current Archaeology* **133**, 18 - 20.

Glendinning, B. 2001 "Wallace Monument replacement floodlighting", *Discovery & Excavation in Scotland* **NS 2**, 97.

Graham, A. 1951 "Archaeological gleanings from Dark-Age records", *Proc Soc Antiq Scot* **85**, 64 - 91.

Greig, J. C. 1970 "Excavations at Castle Point, Troup, Banffshire", *Aberdeen University Review* **43**, 1969-70, 274 – 283.

Greig, J. C. 1971 "Excavations at Cullykhan, Castle Point, Troup, Banffshire", *Scottish Archaeological Forum* **3**, 15 – 21.

Greig, J. C. 1972 "Cullykhan", *Current Archaeology* **32**, 227 – 231.

Hanson, W. S. and Slater, E. A. eds 1991 *Scottish archaeology: new perceptions.* Aberdeen: Aberdeen University Press.

Harding, D. W. 1984 "The function and classification of brochs and duns", in eds Miket, R. and Burgess, C. B., *Between and beyond the Walls: essays on the prehistory and history of northern Britain in honour of George Jobey*, 206 - 220. Edinburgh: John Donald.

Harding, D. W. 1997 "Forts, duns, brochs and crannogs: Iron Age settlements in Argyll", in ed. Ritchie, J. N. G., *The archaeology of Argyll*, 118 - 140. Edinburgh: Edinburgh University Press.

Harding, D. W. and Gilmour, S. M. D. 2000 *The Iron Age settlement at Beirgh, Riof, Isle of Lewis. Excavations, 1985-1995. 1: The structures and stratigraphy.* Edinburgh: University of Edinburgh Department of Archaeology Calanais Research Series No **1**.

Henry, D. ed. 1997 *The worm, the germ and the thorn. Pictish and related essays presented to Isabel Henderson.* Balgavies, Angus: The Pinkfoot Press.

Herrmann, J. (herausgeben von) 1989 *Archäologie in der Deutschen Demokratischen Republik.* Stuttgart: Konrad Theiss. 2 vols.

Hingley, R. 1992 "Society in Scotland from 700 BC to AD 200", *Proc Soc Antiq Scot* **122**, 7 - 53.

Hingley, R. Moore, H. L., Triscott, J. E. and Wilson, G. 1997 "The excavation of two later Iron Age homesteads at Aldclune, Blair Atholl, Perthshire", *Proc Soc Antiq Scot* **127**, 407 - 466.

Hunter, J. R. 1997 *A Persona for the northern Picts.* Rosemarkie: Groam House Museum Trust.

Jansen, H. M. 1992 "The archaeology of Danish commercial centers", in eds Kendall, C. K. and Wells, P. S. *Voyage to the Other World. The legacy of Sutton Hoo*, 171 - 181. Minneapolis: University of Minnesota Press. (= Medieval Studies at Minnesota, **5**).

Jones, S. 1997 *The archaeology of ethnicity: constructing identities in the past and present.* London: Routledge.

Johnson, S. 1984 *A journey to the Western Isles.* Harmondsworth: Penguin (edited by Levi, P.) First published 1775.

Laing, L. R. 1975 *Settlement types in post-Roman Scotland.* Oxford: British Archaeological Reports. = Brit Archaeol Rep, **13**.

Lane, A. 1994 "Trade, gifts and cultural exchange in Dark-Age western Scotland", in ed. Crawford, B. E., *Scotland in Dark Age Europe*, 103 - 115. St Andrews: St John's House Papers, **5**.

Lane, A. and Campbell, E. 2000 *Dunadd: an early Dalriadic capital.* Oxford: Oxbow Books (= Cardiff Studies in Archaeology).

Longley, D. 1975 *Hanging bowls, penannular brooches and the Anglo-Saxon connexion.* Oxford: Brit Archaeol Rep Brit Ser **22**.

Loveluck, C. P. 1998 "A high-status Anglo-Saxon settlement at Flixborough, Lincolnshire", *Antiquity* **72**, 146 - 161.

MacDonald, J. 1861 "Historical notices of 'The Broch' or Burghead in Moray, with a note of its antiquities", *Proc Soc Antiq Scot* **4**, 1860-1, 312 – 369.

Mack, A. 2002 *The association of Pictish symbol stones with ecclesiastical, burial and "memorial" areas*. Balgavies, Angus: Pinkfoot Press.

MacKie, E. W. 1969 "Radiocarbon dates and the Scottish Iron Age", *Antiquity* **43**, 15 – 26.

MacLagan, C. 1875 *The hill forts, stone circles and other structural remains of ancient Scotland*. Edinburgh: Edmonston and Douglas.

McKean, C. 2001 *The Scottish chateau: the country house of Renaissance Scotland*. Stroud: Sutton.

Mercer, R. J. 1991 "The survey of a hilltop enclosure on Ben Griam Beg, Caithness and Sutherland District, Highland Region", in Hanson and Slater, 140 – 152.

Morrison, A. 1974 "Some prehistoric sites in Scotland with medieval occupation", *Scot Archaeol Forum* **6**, 66 - 74.

Murray, H. 1979 "Documentary evidence for domestic buildings in Ireland c. 400 – 1200 in the light of archaeology", *Medieval Archaeology* **23**, 81-97.

Nicolardot, J. P. 1997 "Le camp de Péran à Plédran et la question des remparts vitirifiés" = Annexe, 3 of *Les camps de Myard à Vitteaux et du Châtelet d'Etaules – premiers habitats fortifiés de pierre, de bois et de terre dans leur contexte archéologique*. Unpublished PhD thesis, University of Burgundy / Dijon. 5 vols.

Poleski, J. 1992 "Datierunsgrundlagen der ältesten Phasen des Frühmittelalters (bis zum Ende des 10. Jahrhunderts) in Kleinpolen", in Anon *Probleme der relativen und absoluten Chronologie ab Latènezeit bis zum Frühmittelalter*, 317 - 338. Cracow: Uniwersytet Jagielloński, Institut Archeologii.

R. C. A. H. M. S. 1933 *Eleventh report with inventory of constructions in the counties of Fife, Kinross and Clackmannan*. Edinburgh: HMSO.

R. C. A. H. M. S. 1956 *An inventory of the ancient and historical monuments of Roxburghshire with the fourteenth report of the Commission*. Edinburgh: HMSO. 2 vols.

R. C. A. H. M. S. 1963 *Stirlingshire: an inventory of the ancient monuments*. Edinburgh: HMSO. 2 vols.

R. C. A. H. M. S. 1990 *North-East Perth: an archaeological landscape*. Edinburgh: HMSO.

R. C. A. H. M. S. 1994a *South-East Perth: an archaeological landscape*. Edinburgh: HMSO.

R. C. A. H. M. S. 1994b *Pictish symbol stones: a handlist 1994*. Edinburgh: RCAHMS.

Ralston, I. B. M. 1980 "The Green Castle and the promontory forts of North-East Scotland", *Scott Archaeol Forum* **10**, 1978 (1980), 27 - 40.

Ralston, I. B. M. 1984 "Notes on the archaeology of Kincardine and Deeside District", *The Deeside Field* **18**, 73 - 83.

Ralston, I. B. M. 1986a "The Yorkshire Television vitrified wall experiment at East Tullos, City of Aberdeen District", *Proc Soc Antiq Scot* **116**, 17 - 40.

Ralston, I. B. M. 1986b "The Arbroath Antiquary Club's excavations at Castle Rock promontory fort, Auchmithie, Arbroath and St Vigeans, Angus District", *Proc Soc Antiq Scot* **116**, 101 - 115.

Ralston, I. B. M. 1987a "Portknockie: promontory forts and Pictish settlement in the North-East", in Small, 15 - 26.

Ralston, I. B. M. 1987b "Iron Age to Middle Ages", in *ed.* Omand, D. *The Grampian Book*, 131- 139. Golspie, Sutherland: The Northern Times.

Ralston, I. B. M. 1995 "Fortifications and defence", in *ed.* Green, Miranda, *The Celtic World*, 59 - 81. London: Routledge.

Ralston, I. B. M. 1997 "Pictish homes", in Henry, 18 - 34.

Ralston, I. B. M and Inglis, J. C. 1984 *Foul hordes. The Picts in the North-East and their background.* Aberdeen: Anthrolopogical Museum, Aberdeen University.

Ralston, I. B. M., Sabine, K. A. and Watt, W. G. 1983 "Later prehistoric settlement in North-East Scotland: a preliminary assessment", in Chapman and Mytum, 149 – 173.

Ralston, I. B. M. and Smith, J. S. 1983 "High altitude settlement on Ben Griam Beg, Sutherland", *Proc Soc Antiq Scot* **113**, 636 – 638.

Reynolds, N. M. 1980 "Dark Age timber halls and the background to excavations at Balbridie", *Scottish Archaeological Forum* **10**, 1978 (1980), 41 – 60.

Rideout, J. S., Owen, O. A. and Halpin, E. 1992 *Hillforts of southern Scotland.* Edinburgh: AOC (Scotland) Ltd Monogr **1**

Ritchie, A. 1995a "Meigle and lay patronage in Tayside in the 9th and 10th centuries AD", *Tayside and Fife Archaeol Journ* **1**, 1 - 10.

Ritchie, A. 1995b "The archaeological evidence for daily life", in *ed.* Nicoll, W. H., *A Pictish panorama*, 21 - 26. Balgavies, Angus: The Pinkfoot Press for the Pictish Arts Society.

Ritchie, A. and Ritchie, J. N. G. 1998 *Scotland.* Oxford: Oxford University Press (Oxford Archaeological Guides).

Romilly Allen, J. and Anderson, J. 1903 *The Early Christian monuments of Scotland.* (Reprinted with an introduction by I. Henderson, 1993. Balgavies, Angus: the Pinkfoot Press. 2 vols).

Sanderson, D. C. W., Placido, F. and Tate, J. O. 1988 "Scottish vitrified forts: TL results from six study sites", *Nuclear Tracks and Radiation Measurements* **14**, 307 – 316.

Shaw, I. and Jamieson, R. eds 1999 *A dictionary of archaeology.* Oxford: Blackwell.

Shepherd, I. A. G. 1983 "Pictish settlement problems in north-east Scotland", in Chapman and Mytum, 327 – 356.

Shepherd, I. A. G. 1993 "The Picts in Moray", in *ed.* Sellar, W. D. H., *Moray: province and people*, 75 - 90. Edinburgh: Scottish Society for Northern Studies.

Shepherd, I. A. G. 1996 *Aberdeen and north-east Scotland.* Edinburgh: HMSO. 2 edn.

Shepherd, I. A. G. and Shepherd, A. N. 1978 "An incised Pictish figure and a new symbol stone from Barflat, Rhynie, Gordon District", *Proc Soc Antiq Scot*, **109** (1977-78), 211 – 222.

Simpson, W. D. 1943 *The Province of Mar.* Aberdeen: Aberdeen University Press (= Aberdeen University Studies **121**)

Simpson, W. D. 1954 *Dundarg Castle: a history of the site and a record of the excavations in 1950 and 1951.* Edinburgh: Oliver and Boyd. (= Aberdeen Univ Studies **131**).

Small, A. 1969 "Burghead", *Scot Archaeol Forum* **1**, 61 – 69.

Small, A. 1975 "The hill forts of the Inverness area", in *The hub of the Highlands. The book of Inverness and district*, 78 - 89. Edinburgh: Inverness Field Club / Paul Harris, the Albyn Press.

Small, A. 1976 "Iron Age and Pictish Moray", in *ed*. Omand, D. *The Moray Book*, 113 – 124. Edinburgh: Paul Harris.

Small, A. and Cottam, M. B. 1972 *Craig Phadrig*. Dundee: Univ Dundee Dept Geog Occas Pap, **1**.

Small, A. *ed*. 1987 *The Picts: a new look at old problems*. Dundee: University of Dundee.

Stevenson, J. B. 1985 *Exploring Scotland's heritage: the Clyde Estuary and Central Region*. Edinburgh: HMSO.

Stevenson, J. B. 1991 "Pitcarmicks and fermtouns", *Current Archaeology* **127**, 288 – 291.

Stevenson, R. B. K. 1949 "The nuclear fort of Dalmahoy, Midlothian, and other Dark Age capitals", *Proc Soc Antiq Scot* **83** (1948-49), 186 - 198.

Stevenson, R. B. K. 1972 "Note on mould from Craig Phadrig", in Small and Cottam, 49 - 51.

Taylor, D. B. 1990 *Circular homesteads in north west Perthshire*. Dundee: Abertay Historical Society Publication **29**.

Thomas, C. 1971 *The Early Christian archaeology of North Britain*. Glasgow: Oxford University Press for Glasgow University Publications.

Thomas, C. 1981 *A provisional list of imported pottery in post-Roman western Britain and Ireland*. Redruth: Institute of Cornish Studies Special Report, **7**.

Young, H. W. 1890 "The ancient bath at Burghead, with remarks on its origin, as shewn by existing baths of the same shape and size", *Proc Soc Antiq Scot* **24** (1889-90), 147 - 156.

Young, H. W. 1891 "Notice on the ramparts of Burghead, as revealed by recent excavations", *Proc Soc Antiq Scot* **25**, (1890-91), 436 – 447.

Young, H. W. 1893 "Notes on further excavations at Burghead", *Proc Soc Antiq Scot* **27** (1892-93), 86 - 91.

Ulriksen, J. 1994 "Danish sites and settlements with a maritime context, AD 200-1200", *Antiquity* **68**, 797 - 811.

Wainwright, F. T. 1954 "The ramparts and ditches at Dundarg", in Simpson, 67 – 95.

Wainwright, F. T. *ed*. 1955 *The Problem of the Picts*. Edinburgh: Thomas Nelson.

Watkins, T. F. 1984 "Where were the Picts? An essay in settlement archaeology", in Friell and Watson, 63 - 86.

Webster, L. 1991 "No 247. Horn-mount", in Webster, L. and Backhouse, J. *eds The making of England. Anglo-Saxon art and culture AD 600-900*, 272 - 273. London: British Museum Press.

Wells, P. S. 2001 *Beyond Celts, Germans and Scythians. Archaeology and identity in Iron Age Europe*. London: Duckworth.

Wheeler, R. E. M. 1952 "Earthwork since Hadrian Allcroft", *Archaeol Journ* **106,** (supplement), 62 - 82. = Memorial volume to Sir Alfred Clapham.

Publications available:

Groam House Museum Academic Lecture Series   £4.50.

Anna Ritchie, *Perceptions of the Picts: from Eumenius to John Buchan.*

Barbara Crawford, *Earl & Mormaer, Norse-Pictish relationships in Northern Scotland.*

W.F.H. Nicolaisen, *The Picts and their Place Names.*

John Hunter, *A Persona for the Northern Picts.*

J.N. Graham Ritchie, *Recording Early Christian Monuments in Scotland.*

Sally M. Foster, *Place, Space and Odyssey. Exploring the future of early medieval sculpture.*

Other publications:

Susan E. Seright, *George Bain – master of Celtic Art* £4.50.

The Dream of the Rood, translated and introduced by I.L. Gordon £2.00.

Heron, A Collection of stories for children based in Pictish times £3.00.

These publications are available from:
Groam House Museum, High Street, Rosemarkie IV10 8UF.
Email: groamhouse@ecosse.net
Price includes postage within the UK.